GCSE

DESIGN AND TECHNOLOGY

**Rick Davis
and
Geoff Hancock**

EDUCATIONAL

Letts Educational
Aldine House
Aldine Place
London W12 8AW

Tel: 0181 740 2266
Fax: 0181 743 8451
E-mail: mail@lettsed.co.uk

First published 1997
Reprinted 1998

Text: © Rick Davis and Geoff Hancock 1997

Design and illustrations: © BPP (Letts Educational) Ltd 1994, 1997

British Library Cataloguing in Publication Data
A CIP record for this book is available from the British Library.

ISBN 1 85758 595 X

Acknowledgements

The publishers are grateful to Trevor Bridges for permission to use selected material in Chapter 6.

The authors would like to thank the many students who have inspired us in our careers. This book contains examples of the work of some of them and we gratefully acknowledge this.

We dedicate this book to them and their successors.

We would also like to thank colleagues for help and advice, especially Sue Davis and Tina Hancock for reading and checking the manuscript on numerous occasions.

Rick Davis and Geoff Hancock 1997

Printed in Great Britain by Progressive Printing UK Ltd

Letts Educational is the trading name of BPP (Letts Educational) Ltd

Contents

Introduction

The purpose of this book is to assist you to achieve the best possible grade in GCSE Design and Technology. It is first and foremost a study guide and therefore should be used together with other textbooks and notes supplied by your teacher during your course.

However, the book should be used to establish whether you have covered all aspects required by the assessment criteria and as a source of the basic knowledge and understanding required for success.

Also included are examples of typical questions and suggestions for how to prepare for the examination.

How to use this study guide

- Make sure you know the Examination Board and Area of Focus (if appropriate) you are to be entered for.
- Check the assessment requirements for your examination (see pages 5–10)
- Make yourself aware precisely what percentages of the marks are available for each element of the work and plan to cover them as fully as possible (see Unit 2.4 on time charts).
- Chapter 1 is important as it refers to the key assessment elements and contains information that is common to all themes and may not be repeated in the focus chapters.
- In all cases, 60% of the marks are for coursework. Use Chapter 2 as a guide for what should be included and for methods of presentation.
- Coursework should show your knowledge and understanding, as well as your designing and making skills. Use the relevant chapter on your Area of Focus (see Chapters 3–7) to include all relevant material.
  Note that you are not restricted to one material when producing your coursework and it may be to your advantage to include knowledge and understanding from another Area of Focus to enhance your project. This is particularly true of Chapter 5 which will assist you in the graphical presentation of your work.
- Once your coursework is complete, plan your revision time having found out from your teacher or the examinations officer the date(s) of the paper(s).
- Use the relevant chapter on your Area of Focus (Chapters 3–7) as a guideline for the work needed.
- Practise examination questions under examination conditions – on your own and in strict time allowances – using the specimen questions and worked answers in Chapter 8. Your teacher should be able to provide you with further practice questions.
- It is an advantage to you if you use the 'language' of the subject correctly. Chapter 9 contains a glossary of general terms and their meanings.

Remember, this book cannot be a substitute for the work you have been guided through already in your course. However, if you use it carefully alongside your own work, it will assist you to get the best from the learning that has already happened and allow you to build upon it further.

The examiner will not try to test everything as this would be impossible and unreasonable. The examination questions and the coursework assessment criteria are structured specifically to allow you to display your knowledge and understanding and it is up to you to prepare yourself effectively in order to achieve the best possible grade.

What is the National Curriculum?

The National Curriculum is a set of subjects that applies to all pupils of compulsory school age in maintained schools, and is split into four key stages broadly defined by age range.

- Key Stage 1 is for pupils aged 5–7 (years 1–2)
- Key Stage 2 is for pupils aged 7–11 (years 3–6)
- Key Stage 3 is for pupils aged 11–14 (years 7–9)
- Key Stage 4 is for pupils aged 14–16 (years 10–11)

For each subject, and for each key stage, there are programmes of study which set out what should be taught and attainment targets which set out the standards expected by levels. You should remember that each Key Stage should not be treated in isolation. The work undertaken in Key Stage 4 will build upon the knowledge and understanding gained in the earlier key stages. At Key Stage 4, public examinations are the main means of assessing attainment and all pupils will have been prepared for such examinations since 1 August 1996 for year 10.

What is National Curriculum technology?

There are two attainment targets for GCSE Design and Technology:

1 Designing
2 Making

The programme of study at Key Stage 4 requires pupils to be given opportunities to develop their design and technology capability through:

- designing and making products
- activities related to industrial practices, including the application of systems and control
- focused practical tasks which develop and practise particular skills and knowledge
- activities in which they investigate, disassemble and evaluate familiar products and applications
- applying skills, knowledge and understanding from other subjects

It also requires that pupils should be taught:

- designing skills
- making skills
- materials and components
- systems and control
- products and applications
- quality
- health and safety

In addition, pupils should be given opportunities, where appropriate, to develop and apply their information technology (IT) capability in their study of Design and Technology.

How is it assessed at Key Stage 4: GCSE?

Although there is a core body of knowledge and understanding, the Examination Boards have addressed the programmes of study through a number of focus areas.

This study guide will concentrate on the areas of:

- electronic products
- food technology
- graphic products
- resistant materials technology
- textiles technology

There are also two forms of certification:

1 **Full course**

   This is a full GCSE, usually taught in 8–10% of curriculum time (2–2.5 hours per week) over the full two years of Key Stage 4. This will give you five full terms in which to complete your course.

2 **Short course**

   This is credited as being the equivalent of a half GCSE. It is usually taught in 5% of curriculum time for the full two years, or for about 10% of time for one year. If you have embarked on the latter option, you must plan your time even more carefully as your course will effectively be only two terms long as the coursework deadlines and examination dates are during the third (summer) term. You must be aware that if you are sitting the short course, the standards remain the same as for the full course, it is only the content that is reduced.

For the written examination, you will be entered by your teacher for one of two tiers. You must be aware that the tier of entry will be based on your ability to answer examination questions and not your performance in the coursework element, which has a single tier of entry. The two tiers of entry have limits for the possible grades to be awarded:

Tier	Grades available
Higher	A*–D
Foundation	C–G

Candidates failing to achieve a grade G in the foundation tier, or grade D in the higher tier will be reported as Unclassified (U). It is therefore critical that you discuss your tier of entry with your teacher so as not to jeopardise your final grade.

The difference between the Foundation and Higher tiers

In the case of the coursework there is no *difference* at all as it will be marked using the same assessment criteria. You must therefore make every effort to cover all aspects of the assessment criteria, full details of which will be available from your teacher.

The major difference occurs with the terminal examination. Your teacher will enter you for one of the two tiers depending on your level of competence in this element of the examination, regardless of your performance in the coursework element.

As already noted, this is a critical decision since you will be reported as unclassified (U) if your fail to reach the minimum mark required for the tier you have been entered for.

It should be noted that there is no difference in the syllabus content between the two tiers of entry.

However, there will be a difference in the difficulty of the questions asked and the depth of the answers required between the two tiers. In Chapter 8, the specimen questions have been marked (F) for foundation tier, (F/H) for questions suitable for both tiers and (H) for those questions intended for the higher tier only.

You will see from pages 5–10 that there may also be a difference in the number and the length of the examination papers between the two tiers. You are advised to check this carefully with your teacher, especially if you are being taught in a group where the students are being entered for different tiers.

The difference between full and short courses

As can be seen from pages 5–10, the major difference in terms of coursework is the amount of time that is to be spent on it, as the designing and making skills required will largely be the same.

However, the syllabus content for knowledge and understanding will be reduced for the short course and the thus the questions set by the examiner in the examination will reflect this.

It should be noted that this study guide has been written with the full course in mind. You are therefore advised to check carefully with your teacher, and the particular syllabus that you are studying, what precisely is included in terms of content for a short course.

Examination Board information and requirements

The following pages contain the assessment structures for the six major examining groups for England and Wales. It should be noted that changes do take place from time to time and you are advised to verify the information for your particular course.

It should be noted that only information regarding the following areas of focus is included:

- electronic products
- food technology
- graphic products
- resistant materials technology
- textiles technology

The requirements for other areas of focus may be different and you should carefully check this with your teacher.

The Examining Boards in Scotland and Northern Ireland have markedly different assessment arrangements in this area of the National Curriculum. However, this book can still be used effectively as a revision guide for candidates sitting examinations in related subjects, with respect to the knowledge content and the advice on coursework.

You are therefore advised to check carefully the syllabus requirements of the course you are taking in order to seek out the relevant elements.

Scottish Qualifications Authority – SQA (formerly SEB) Ironmills Road, Dalkeith, Midlothian, EH22 1EL (Tel: 0131 663 6601).

Northern Ireland Council for the Curriculum Examinations and Assessment – (CCEA) Clarendon Dock, 29 Clarendon Road, Belfast BT1 3BG (Tel: 01232 261200).

EDEXCEL (London Examinations)

London Examinations – Edexcel Foundation (formerly ULEAC)
Stewart House
32 Russell Square
London
WC1B 5DN

Tel: 0171 331 4000

Full Course

Terminal Examination

Foundation Tier	Paper	2 hrs	(Graphic Products – 2 hrs 30 mins)	40%
Higher Tier	Paper	2 hrs	(Graphic Products – 2 hrs 30 mins)	40%

Coursework

Project   40% – representing not less than 30 hours work
Investigation   20% – representing not less than 10 hours work

Designing 40%
Making 60%

Short Course

Terminal Examination

Foundation Tier	Paper	1 hr	(Graphic Products – 1 hr 30 mins)	40%
Higher Tier	Paper	1 hr	(Graphic Products – 1 hr 30 mins)	40%

Coursework

Project   – 40% – representing not less than 15 hours work
Investigation – 20% – representing not less than 5 hours work

Designing 40%
Making 60%

MEG

Midland Examining Group
Syndicate Buildings
1 Hills Road
Cambridge
CB1 2EU

Tel : 01223 553311

Full Course

Terminal Examination

Foundation Tier	Paper 1	1 hr	(Graphic Products – 1 hr 15 mins)	20%
	Paper 3	1 hr	(Graphic Products – 1 hr 15 mins)	20%
Higher Tier	Paper 2	1 hr 15 mins	(Graphic Products – 1 hr 30 mins)	20%
	Paper 4	1 hr 15 mins	(Graphic Products – 1 hr 30 mins)	20%

Papers 3 and 4 will include a compulsory product evaluation question, set on a different theme each year.

Coursework

Project 60% – representing 40/50 hours work

Designing 40%
Making 60%

Short Course

Terminal Examination

Foundation Tier	Paper 1	1 hr	(Graphic Products – 1 hr 15 mins)	40%
Higher Tier	Paper 2	1 hr 15 mins	(Graphic Products – 1 hr 30 mins)	40%

There will be no choice of questions.

Coursework

Project 60% – representing 20/25 hours work

Designing 40%
Making 60%

NEAB

Northern Examinations and Assessment Board
Wheatfield Road
Westerhope
Newcastle upon Tyne
NE5 5JZ

Tel : 0191 2010180

Note This is the administering office for Design and Technology

Full Course

Terminal Examination

Foundation Tier	Paper	2 hrs	40%
Higher Tier	Paper	2 hrs 30 mins	40%

A preparation sheet giving advance notice of the context for the paper will be issued to candidates on or after 1 March in the year of the examination.

Coursework
Project 60% – representing 40/50 hours work

Designing 40%
Making 60%

Short Course

Terminal Examination

Foundation Tier	Paper	1 hr 30 mins	40%
Higher Tier	Paper	2 hrs	40%

A preparation sheet giving advance notice of the context for the paper will be issued to candidates on or after 1 March in the year of the examination.

Coursework
Project 60% – representing 20/25 hours work

Designing 40%
Making 60%

RSA

RSA Examinations Board
Westwood Way
Coventry
CV4 8HS

Tel : 01203 470033

Full Course

Terminal Examination

Foundation Tier	Paper 1	Core – 1 hr	20%
	Paper 2	Area of Focus Extension – 1 hr	20 %
Higher Tier	Paper 1	Core – 1 hr	20%
	Paper 2	Area of Focus Extension – 1 hr	20 %

Papers 1 and 2 are based on a design scenario set by the RSA.
Paper 2 will concern a design specification in the industrial manufacturing material chosen.

The 40% of marks for the examination are divided equally between Designing and Making.

Coursework
Project 60% – representing approximately 40 hours work

Designing 33.3%
Making 66.7%

Short Course

Terminal Examination

Foundation Tier	Paper	1 hr	40%
Higher Tier	Paper	1 hr	40%

The paper is the same as Paper 1 taken by the full course candidates.

Coursework
Project 60% – representing approximately 20 hours work

Designing 33.3%
Making 66.7%

SEG

Southern Examining Group
Stag Hill House
Guildford
Surrey
GU2 5XJ

Tel : 01483 506506

Full Course

Terminal Examination

Foundation Tier	Paper 1	Common Syllabus Content – 1 hr 30 mins
	Paper 2	Area of Focus – 1 hr
Higher Tier	Paper 1	Common Syllabus Content – 1 hr 30 mins
	Paper 2	Area of Focus – 1 hr

All questions will be compulsory.

Where appropriate, study topics will be issued to candidates in the spring term of the year of the examination.

Coursework
Project 60% – representing 40 hours work

Coursework submission achieved through the Common Syllabus Content and *one* Area of Focus.

Designing 40%
Making 60%

Short Course

Terminal Examination

Foundation Tier	Paper	Common Syllabus Content – 1hr 30 mins
Higher Tier	Paper	Common Syllabus Content – 1hr 30 mins

All questions will be compulsory.

Where appropriate, study topics will be issued to candidates in the spring term of the year of the examination.

These papers are the same as Paper 1 taken by the full course candidates.

Coursework
    Project – 60% weighting – representing 20 hours work

  Note Choice of material areas from the common Syllabus Content only – ceramics, food, resistant materials, textiles.

WJEC

Welsh Joint Education Committee
245 Western Avenue
Cardiff
CF5 2YX

Tel : 01222 265000

Full Course

Terminal Examination

Foundation Tier	Paper 1	Core – 1 hr	16%
	Paper 2	Area of Focus – 1 hr 30 mins	24%
Higher Tier	Paper 1	Core – 1 hr	16%
	Paper 2	Area of Focus – 1 hr 30 mins	24%

Coursework
    Project 60% – representing approximately 40 hours work

    Designing 40%
    Making 60%

Short Course

Terminal Examination

Foundation Tier	Paper	Core – 1 hr 30 mins	40%
Higher Tier	Paper	Core – 1 hr 30 mins	40%

This paper is common to all Areas of Focus.

Coursework
    Project 60% – representing approximately 20 hours work.

    Designing 40%
    Making 60%

  Note Electronics must be taken as a GCSE (Combined Syllabus) and therefore is not available as a short course.

Chapter 1
Key assessment elements

The National Curriculum for Design and Technology lists seven key assessment skills that all GCSE syllabuses have to cover. These are:

- designing skills
- making skills
- materials and components
- systems and control
- products and applications
- quality
- health and safety

Skills are things that you have proved that you can do, therefore you will need to show both in your coursework and in the examination that you have acquired them. *Read through Chapter 2 on coursework and see if you can identify where these key assessment skills occur.*

1.1 Designing skills

Central to success within design and technology is your ability to design solutions to identified problems. In order to do this you need to have a clear understanding of the design process. A useful model of this process is given in Fig. 1.1.

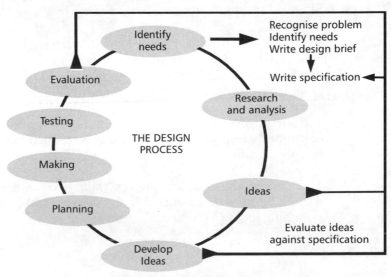

Fig 1.1 The Design Process model

You would normally start at the top of the circle 'problem identification' but it is possible to start anywhere around the circle, e.g. evaluating an existing product may lead to a design problem to be solved.

The design process in action – the birth of a new electric jug kettle

When Tefal, a French company, wanted a design for the first cordless electric jug kettle it went to a British design company to produce it. The development of the kettle, from the first idea to mass production of the final product, took nine months and went through the following stages.

Stage 1 Developing a design brief and specification

Tefal set down what it wanted the designers to produce in the form of a specification. The specification included all the key design features needed including

- that the kettle should be cordless
- that existing components should be used (e.g. the element)

Stage 2 Investigation research and testing

The designers looked at every kettle on the market and took them apart (known as product disassembly) in order to find out:

- what they were made of and why
- how they were designed and made
- what their strengths and weaknesses were
- what the design problems were
- information about safety devices
- about current style and fashion

Stage 3 Generating a design proposal

The designers produced a wide range of sketches of jug designs. These were evaluated and revealed that the new designs could not use existing parts after all – they were too big. Foam plastic models of the kettle were produced with exploded designs of the working parts so that Tefal's engineers and marketing people could assess them.

Stage 4 Development

Once the company had settled on its preferred design, an accurate non-working model was made so that work on producing the tooling needed for mass production could begin. This took months. In the meantime, designs for the graphics were finalised. The working drawings were completed, costings checked and production plans and schedules finalised. The factory in France was 'tooled up' and a run of 250 kettles made. These were used to check quality and get the consumer's response. Minor changes were then made before the factory went into full production.

This case study shows the design skills that are needed in the process of product design. Because designing skills are so important in this subject you should practise sketching ideas to problems.

As part of your revision, design some of the following:

- 10 useful things to do with a paper clip
- a fold up toothbrush
- packaging for disposable razors
- a nutritionally balanced healthy snack bar
- a uniform for a fast food restaurant
- a savoury bread product
- a young child's play outfit
- a jig for drilling equidistant holes in a 20mm wide strip of mild steel

1.2 Making skills

There are three parts to the making skills element:

- planning the making
- maintaining quality, health and safety
- effective making

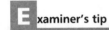

Examiner's tip

Keep a sketchbook with you all the time – keep drawing anything of interest

Planning the making

In order to achieve a high grade for planning, you must produce an accurate schedule for the making of your designs. Schedules indicate the **sequence** of tasks, the **time required** for each task together with details of all tools, components and processes used. This is a very important stage in the design process; refer to Chapter 2 for examples of planning schedules.

Maintenance of quality, health and safety

There are three aspects to this which you need to know for the examination and be able to demonstrate in your coursework. These are:

- the difference between quality control and quality assurance
- how products are manufactured in quantity
- how to evaluate the quality of products

Quality control means *checking for accuracy*, e.g. size, consistency, weight, etc.

Quality assurance means *building in procedures* which ensure that a certain quality is achieved at various stages, e.g. setting the depth stop on a drill, sensory analysis tests of food products.

Manufacturing in quantity. You need to know that there are different scales of production. These are given below with alternative descriptions in italics.

- One off *(job production)*. One or a very few hand-made/crafted items. These are usually expensive because of time taken to manufacture them and the need for skilled workers.
- Batch production *(batch flow)*. A low-level production, e.g. 20–500 – jigs and other time-saving devices are used to ensure consistency.
- Repetitive batch *(flow)*. Repeat batches – where production runs are repeated when required, such as with seasonal products.
- Continuous production *(flow)*. Only used when 1000s of products are required continually. This type of production often involves a high initial outlay on machines and equipment and is less reliant upon skilled workers – computer-aided manufacturing (CAM) is often used.

Evaluating the quality of products

You should evaluate the quality of products by using criteria such as:

- appropriateness of the material used
- accuracy of manufacture
- appropriateness of finish
- how well it functions
- aesthetics – appearance, taste, smell, feel
- legal requirements in terms of health and safety specifications to be met

Effective making

Chapter 2 details tips on making for your coursework.

Examiner's tip

Take great care when designing a product. Making always takes a long time and one of the most common reasons for students failing to get high grades is that the project is too demanding and remains unfinished.

1.3 Materials and components

This unit is fully covered in Chapters 3–7 and relates specifically to the GCSE material area you are studying.

1.4 Systems and control

The definition of a system is a number of parts which are connected together in order to perform a function. Control involves one device controlling the movement or action of an independent device connected to it.

Basic principles of control

Control is an essential part of our lives. The best way of understanding how control works is by using a systems approach. The three basic units of any system are input; control; output.

Fig 1.2

Common examples of this are:

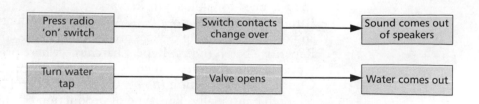

Fig. 1.3

An input is usually some kind of movement, e.g. pressing a switch, turning a key or a change in the environment, for example temperature rise, change in volume or light level.

The **control** may be changing the size of the input, e.g. an amplifier increasing the sound level in a Hi-Fi system or changing the input into a different form, for example a rise in temperature automatically opening a greenhouse window.

The output could be in the form of movement, e.g., an electric motor, sound, e.g., a loudspeaker, light or heat.

The most simple form of control system is called an open loop system.

Fig. 1.4

In this system, tiny electrical signals from the record player are amplified and converted into sound by the loudspeakers. The problem with open loop systems is that they do not give any control over the output. For example, in the system shown there is no volume control; in this system you would not be able to turn the sound up or down. The solution to this problem is to use feedback. A system which uses feedback is called a closed loop system.

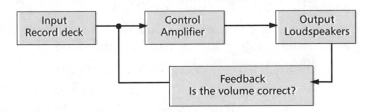

Fig. 1.5

In this simple closed loop system, the feedback is provided by the person who manually adjusts the volume. More complex systems adjust themselves, these are called control systems.

Common examples of control systems:

Household central heating system

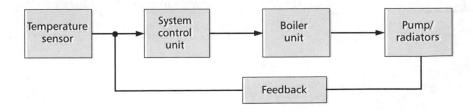

Fig. 1.6

In this system the temperature sensor detects that the room is too cold. The control unit switches on the boiler which pumps hot water into the radiators. As the room heats up the temperature sensor input causes the control unit to switch the boiler off. As the room cools, the boiler is switched back on, etc. The system continually loops around maintaining the correct temperature.

Control systems often have to make decisions. For example, in the central heating system above, this would normally have a clock or timer fitted so that the system would work only when it was cold and it was the correct time.

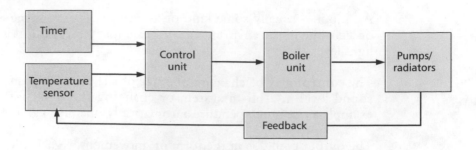

Fig. 1.7

The decisions that control systems have to take can be shown as a logic diagram or truth table. For a full explanation of logic circuits see Chapter 3.

1.5 Products and applications

'Candidates should be taught to analyse products, their application and manufacturing situations through disassembly and evaluation.' (*National Curriculum Key Stage 4 statement.*)

This is something that you should have done within your course and involves understanding about materials and design by looking at existing products and applications.

- **A product is:** something which has functioning parts and which meets a need (it could be historical as well as contemporary).

- **An application is:** using a product for a purpose or identifying a need for a product.

- **Disassembly is:** mentally or physically undressing a product in order to see how it was made/assembled, the materials/processes used, design features, form and function. Disassembly is often called product analysis.

(See Chapter 2 for further examples of product investigation and disassembly.)

E **xaminer's tip**

Use the specification in Chapter 2 as a framework for disassembling a product.

1.6 Quality

In order to gain a high grade in design and technology you must demonstrate quality in both designing and making. In order to do this you must first appreciate what quality is. You should identify common features of quality products from looking at your own and others' work. These criteria will include:

- **Aesthetics.** Sensory qualities including touch, smell, and taste. The visual quality using such criteria as shape, form, balance, symmetry, proportion, rhythm – how are these features combined to make such a pleasing product?

- **Function.** How well does the product perform its intended task/s? Is it reliable? Consistent?

- **Materials.** Are the best materials/ingredients used in terms of strength, aesthetics appropriateness? Are they used sympathetically?

- **Accuracy.** How precisely are parts made? How does this contribute to reliability?

1.7 Health and safety

Health and safety is an important aspect of all product development and you need to recognise how designers and manufacturers have considered health and safety legislation within existing products. Disassembly activities could identify:

- child-proof products – no tiny parts that could be swallowed, lead paint/toxic materials in toys, finger, hand and head traps
- inherent dangers with electrical goods
- fire-retardant materials for textile products
- health and hygiene regulations concerned with the storage and preparation of food products
- safe working practices when using hand and machine tools.

You should include health and safety considerations at a number of key stages in your major project. Evidence within your portfolio could include:

- Research. Look at sources such as British Standards Institute (BSI), Institute of Environmental Health Officers, 1991 Food Act, Containment of Substances Hazardous to Health (COSHH).
- Specification. Include specific health and safety considerations for your product.
- Designing. Is your idea safe for the intended user? What health and safety implications might there be in manufacturing?
- Production schedule. Detail health and safety procedures during making – safety equipment, i.e. gloves, goggles, machine guards, temperature control of food, chilling, freezing requirements, etc.
- Evaluation. You must include a health and safety review – how you carried out the health and safety procedures and how effective they were during the making process.

Chapter 2
Coursework

'Pupils should be taught to develop their design and technology capability through combining their *designing* and *making skills* with *knowledge and understanding*, in order to design and make products.'

National Curriculum Key Stage 4 statement

It is through the coursework element of your course that you will most readily satisfy this statement.

E **xaminer's tip**

Remember this motto as a recipe for success at GCSE – `simple things, well designed, beautifully made'.

2.1 General requirements

All Examination Boards require a significant amount of coursework which you will normally undertake during the final two terms of your course. However, by this stage your teacher will have asked you to carry out a number of minor projects which will have prepared you for this task. It is important that you put your full effort into these pieces of work, because there are certain circumstances when they may be used for assessment towards your final coursework mark, e.g. prolonged absence during your final year through injury or illness.

For your assessed coursework elements, there may be a restriction on the size and quantity of your submission. Check carefully what is required by your particular Examination Board before you start work and plan accordingly (see pages 5-10). During the marking of this coursework, an additional 5% will be awarded for spelling, punctuation and grammar. It is important, therefore, that you take every care to check your work thoroughly for these aspects, both during and at the end in order not to lose marks unnecessarily.

E **xaminer's tip**

This is an extremely important element of the examination, carrying up to 60% of the marks available. However, it is also the element over which you have complete control. Having chosen your project, use your time wisely and efficiently to carry it out to the best of your ability.

It is important to remember that your teacher will have to sign that the work presented for assessment is all your own. The moderation procedure will also check on this. It is worth noting that any work submitted that cannot be authenticated by the teacher, or is considered unlikely to be by you, may be removed from your submission. In extreme circumstances, the Examination Board may take further action which could jeopardise your other examination entries.

2.2 Choosing a project for success

There are basically two types of project:

1   Individual projects – in this case you will carry out the project on your own, seeking advice and assistance from your teacher or relevant experts. This is the most common situation and preferred by the Examiner.

2   Group projects – because you may feel more confident working with another student or group of students, or your school's circumstances require it, projects that are made up of a number of smaller elements that together create a much larger outcome are allowed. Remember, however, you may not 'own' the end result!

Points to consider when choosing a project :

Do

- choose a project that interests you and that you can sustain for the length of time available
- check with your teacher that you will be able to cover all the assessment objective
- choose a project that will allow you to work mainly in a medium that you are most skilled in
- make sure before you start that the outcome is achievable in the time available

Don't

- start with the outcome. 'I want to make a . . .' is an unpromising beginning
- choose what your friend has decided to do, he/she may have a real interest and expertise that you don't possess

2.3 Presentation methods

Page layout

It is an advantage if you can personalise your work and create a style of presentation that makes it easy to follow:

- keep a consistent style throughout
- simple borders are more effective
- title blocks should not dominate the page
- limit the use of colours used on a page
- number pages after completing the project
- plan the use of the space available to avoid overcrowding or large blank areas.
- use underlays with grids and lines to align your work

Examiner's tip

When working on a group project, you must make certain that you have covered all aspects of the assessment objectives in your own presentation and not rely on another student to carry out any part of it. You can only be marked on the evidence submitted of your own work.

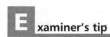

Examiner's tip

The best projects tend to be 'real' ones. That is a project that is generated by a need that someone has brought to your notice. This has the added advantage of having someone else who can act as a consultant throughout the project, help generate the specification, test the outcome and provide effective evaluation.

Examiner's tip

Use the most appropriate form of communication for the aspect of the project you are dealing with.
This certainly will also be the most effective in terms of the time you need to spend. You should also include a wide range of methods, not just concentrate on one form of communication.

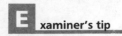

E **xaminer's tip**

Unnecessary embellishment of borders and titles wastes valuable time and will gain you no marks.

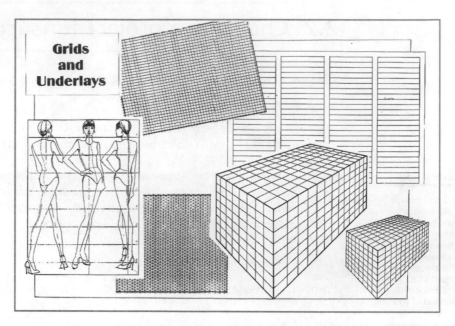

Fig 2.1 Examples of underlays to assist page layout

The written word

At times you will need to include substantial passages of writing. However, you should avoid the mistake of writing about everything, especially if it is not relevant to the progress of the project. Remember, a fully annotated sketch can often be far more appropriate.

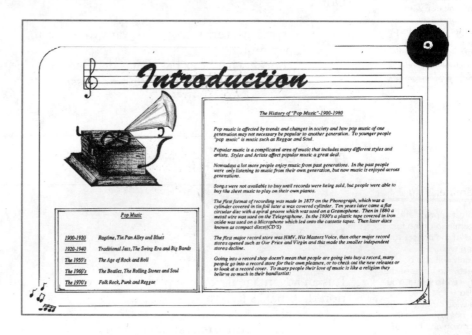

Fig. 2.2 Examples of illustrated written elements

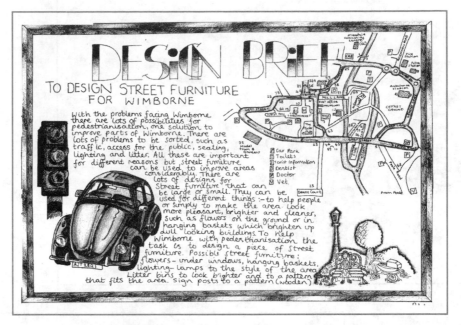

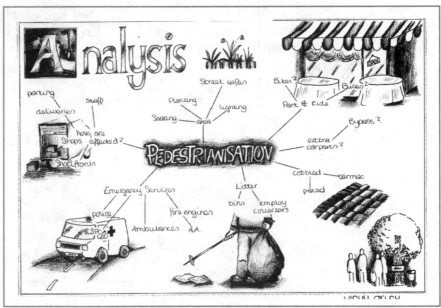

Fig. 2.2 Examples of illustrated written elements (continued)

Large passages of text may be well worth word processing. This has the advantage of taking up less space, is generally quicker to produce, can be readily corrected or edited and is easier to store until required. However, don't get carried away! Unless your handwriting is very poor indeed, word processed annotations that are then cut up and stuck adjacent to the relevant illustrations are an inefficient use of your time.

Bubble charts and spider diagrams

Brainstorming, where you just list anything that comes into your head that could possibly be relevant to the topic under consideration, is a common method of starting off. Rather than just having a list, it can be more effective to present your thoughts in the form of a diagram that can let you determine connections between the various thoughts and their relative importance. This method will often lead you to notice omissions or possible areas for further consideration.

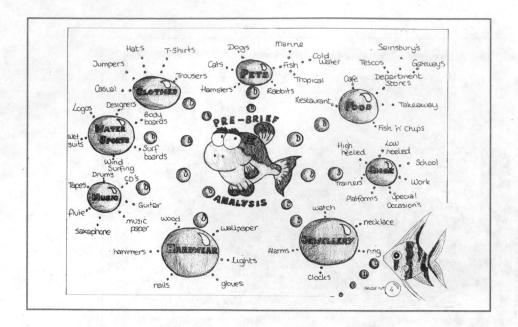

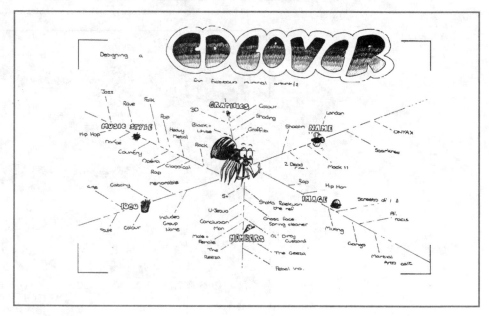

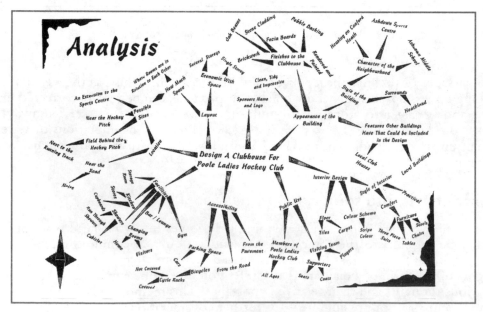

Fig. 2.3 Examples of spider diagrams

Freehand drawing (sketching)

The advantages of using annotated sketches have already been noted. Freehand sketching should be used at all times other than for working drawings or final developments where accuracy is required. For more on graphic techniques see Chapter 5.

Points to remember:

- try to sketch in three dimensions – isometric is often the most useful method
- avoid using soft pencils as these will smudge easily
- start off by lightly drawing the box the item would fit in (crating out), and slowly putting in the basic features – then darken up the required lines and add rendering as necessary
- don't use fine liners unless you are very confident and competent, except for highlighting noteworthy aspects
- it is not always necessary to fully render or even complete sketches as long as they have adequately communicated the point being made

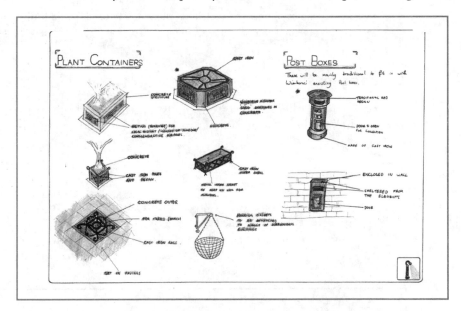

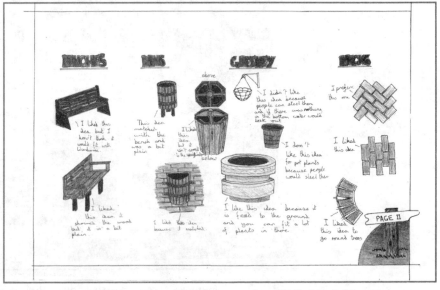

Fig. 2.4 Examples of freehand sketching with notation used to add further information or make comments

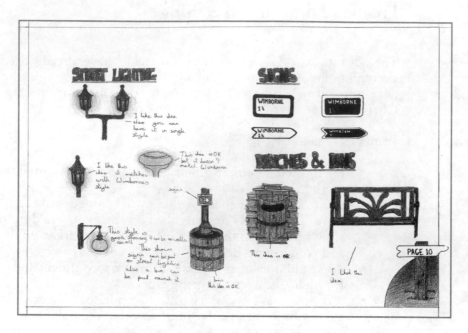

Fig. 2.4 Examples of freehand sketching with notation used to add further information or make comments (continued)

Cut and paste

You will often collect a lot of clippings, cuttings and pictures from magazines and leaflets during the project which can usefully be used in your presentation.

Points to remember:

- avoid haphazard display, cut and mount with care
- be selective, only use directly relevant material
- always annotate your chosen illustrations otherwise they will gain no credit

Fig. 2.5 Examples of cut and paste using photographs and clippings

Fig. 2.5 Examples of cut and paste using photographs and clippings (continued)

Photographs

Although expensive, the inclusion of photographs will indicate first-hand research and will be of particular relevance to your chosen project. They will also provide a permanent record of work you have done that may otherwise be lost.

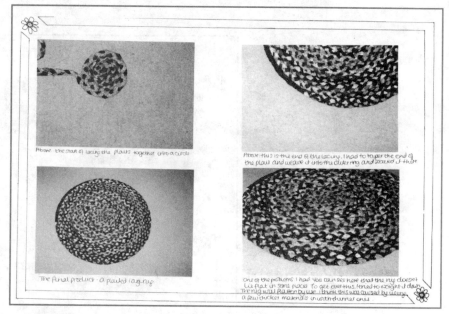

Fig. 2.6 Photographs recording aspects of manufacture

Scanned and photocopied images

These can be extremely useful when you are unable to destroy the source material, e.g. a library book. Remember, however, to include the source of the material in a bibliography.

Tracing and copying

These are useful ways of obtaining the basic shape of complex images that you may have difficulty in drawing yourself.

Methods include:

- lightboxes
- tracing paper
- layout paper

Questionnaires

Questionnaires should be used to gather a wide range of opinion about a particular topic. It is especially useful at the research and evaluation stages of the project.

Points to remember:

- seek the views of people who have a direct connection to the topic of the questionnaire, or your results could be misleading
- be clear what you intend to find out
- decide how many people you need to question
- start with 'yes/no' questions
- multiple-choice questions should have a space for 'other' answers
- plan the questionnaire so that it is in a logical order and does not take too long
- allow space(s) for comments
- thank your respondents!

Charts, tables and graphs

These are the best way to handle information gained from surveys, questionnaires and tests. They can be presented graphically or produced by a computer program.

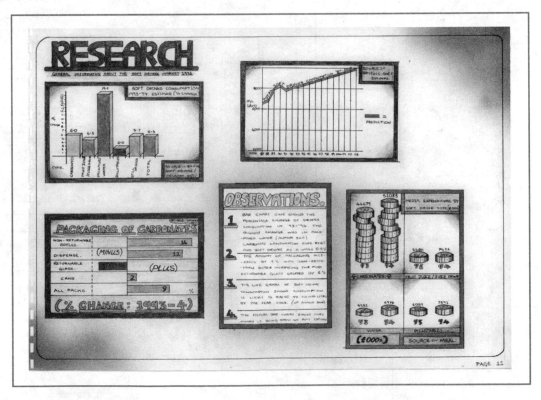

Fig. 2.7 Examples of questionnaires and their results presented as graphs and charts

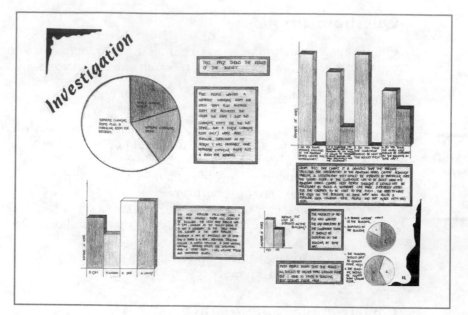

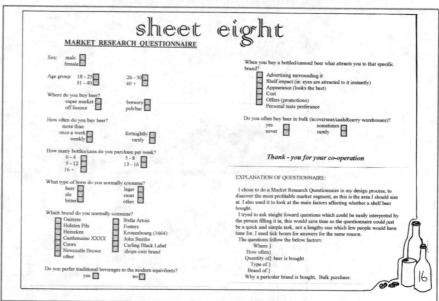

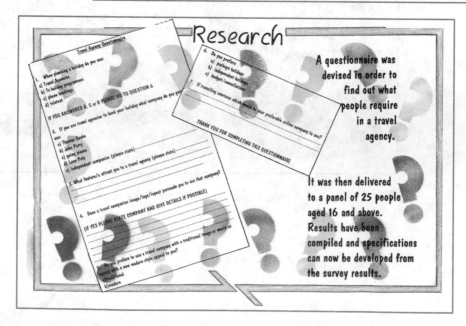

Fig. 2.7 Examples of questionnaires and their results presented as graphs and charts
(continued)

Working Drawings

The main purpose of these is to give all the necessary information required to make your design.

Any method of drawing is acceptable, but the following must be included:

- dimensions
- materials
- construction details
- parts list
- finishes

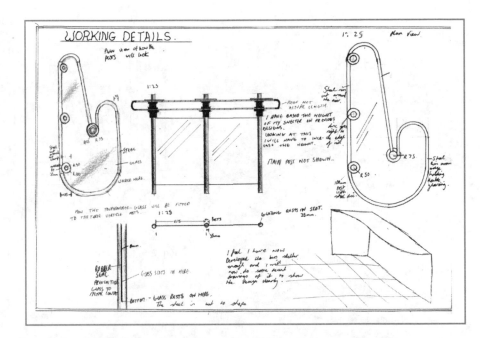

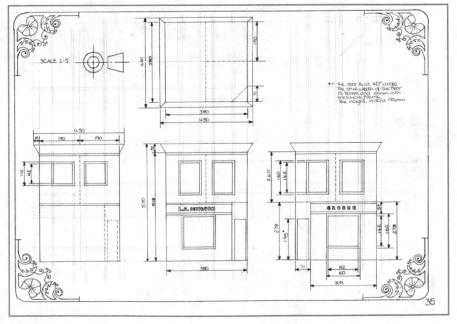

Fig. 2.8 Examples of working drawings

E **xaminer's tip**

Never discard a sheet that
has a mistake on it, It is
perfectly acceptable to paste
on a corrected version and
even make a feature of it by
such techniques as double
mounting.

Mistakes

You will always make mistakes during your project. Try to correct small errors as neatly as possible, but avoid large areas of crossing out or the use of correcting fluid as it looks unsightly.

Gaining more space on your paper

You may wish to display all the work relating to a single topic on one sheet of paper. This can be achieved by the use of pockets, folding and layering.

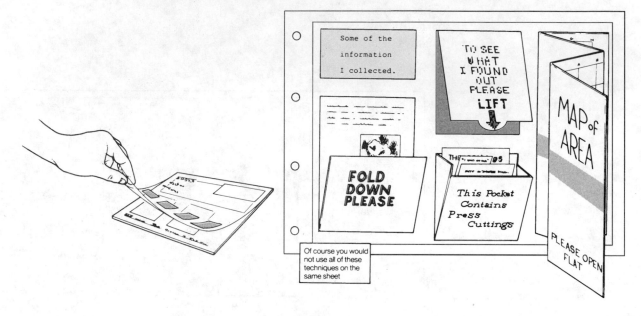

Fig. 2.9 Methods of gaining extra space

E **xaminer's tip**

It is essential that you cover
all aspects of the assessment
objectives. You must avoid
spending too
long on any one unit,
however well it is done, as it
will not compensate for
incomplete, rushed or
missing units.

2.4 Managing the project

Points to remember:

- produce a time chart for the whole of the project on which you include such things as – holidays, mock examinations, other school events and deadlines
- allow slack time for such things as – awaiting replies to letters, arranging visits, developing photographs, access to specialist facilities, e.g. computer room

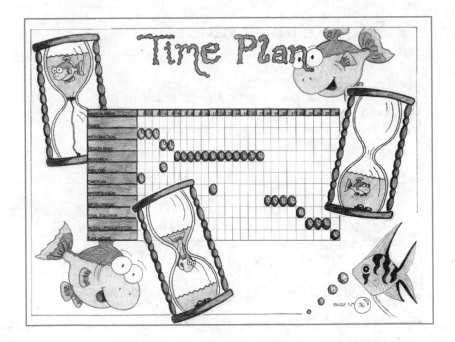

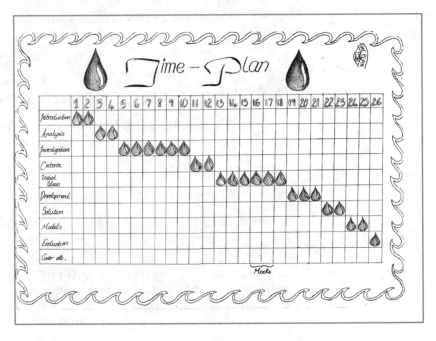

Fig. 2.10   Examples of time charts for projects

- maintain a project notebook to be presented with the folio. This should be a true account of your progress throughout the entire project and should include:

  - diary of events
  - thoughts and conversations
  - addresses and telephone numbers
  - sketches
  - cuttings, etc.
  - important things to remember or do at a later stage

2.5 Choosing a situation or need

This is a very important stage because it forms the introduction to your project and in it you must demonstrate to the examiner that your project involves a real problem which is worth while and not contrived.

The design problem might be identified from one of the following:

- an activity, interest or hobby you are involved with
- a need in the community, local business or school
- something set by your teacher
- something suggested by the Examination Board

The introduction could include:

- some background information on your involvement with the problem
- details of how the need has arisen
- why you consider it to be a worthwhile activity

2.6 Preparing a design brief and specification

The design brief:

- should be a short statement of the problem to be solved
- should not describe the outcome

The specification represents an analysis of the brief. This is very important as it defines the things that your final solution must satisfy in order to be considered a successful design. Your specification should demonstrate that you understand the needs of the problem you have identified.

The following should be considered in your product specification:

- Context
  - Where and how will the product be used?
  - What are the implications for the selection of materials?

- Aesthetics
  - colour and texture
  - styling, feel, taste, smell
  - size, shape, proportion, balance

- Performance
  - function – how it works and why
  - ergonomic/anthropometric considerations
  - secondary functions – quality, reliability, safety, fashion, efficiency

- Production
  - costing
  - scale of production
  - timescale

- Maintenance
  - how will it be maintained?

Fig. 2.11 Examples of product specification presented as a list

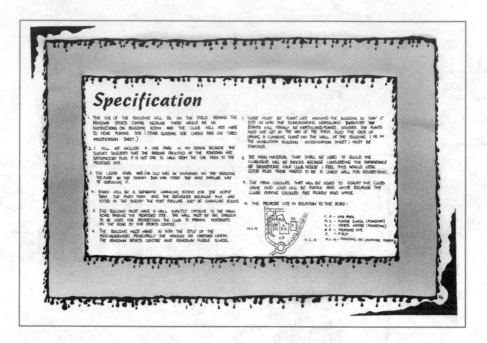

Fig. 2.11 Examples of a product specification presented as a list (continued)

2.7 Analysing and researching

This involves investigating your chosen problem or need and thus adding depth and further information to your specification. Research is an important part of the process of design because it provides the knowledge and understanding needed to make decisions.

At all times you must take account of the fact that your design would need to be produced industrially. Therefore your research must consider how similar products are manufactured commercially in order for you to be able to make informed design decisions.

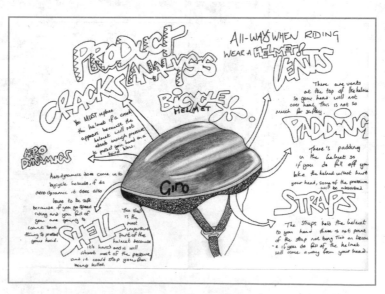

Fig. 2.12 Examples of product analysis

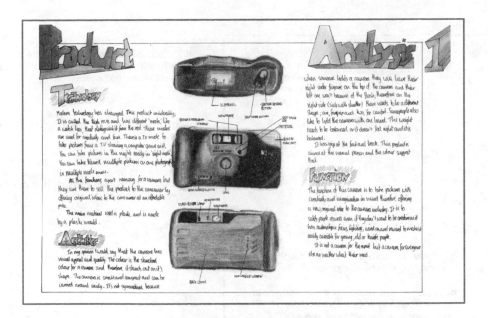

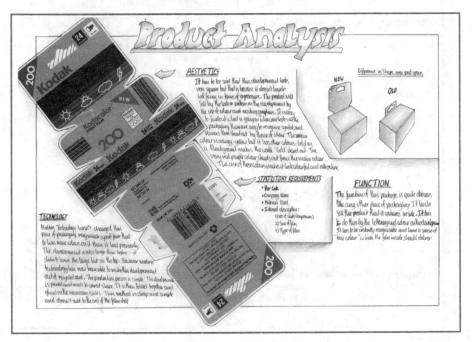

Fig. 2.12 Examples of product analysis (continued)

Points to remember:

- include *only* relevant information
- use a wide variety of sources
- write letters to people who may have relevant knowledge (see Fig. 2.13)
- analyse similar products
- critically analyse the information you acquire
- always draw conclusions from your research
- go back to your initial specification and adapt as necessary

Letter	Guidance
School Name Education Road Town County Post Code	If the school policy allows, use the school's own headed paper. Otherwise, use the school's address with permission
Date	Write as early as possible – replies can be slow!
Named Person Relevant Company Industry Road Town Country Post Code	It is an advantage to write to a particular person. If you do not have a name, to a post-holder connected with your project. If in doubt, write to 'Customer relations'.
Dear Sir/Madam	
I am a Year 11 student studying GCSE Technology and at present I am working on my major project which is concerned with ….	Say who you are and what you are doing.
I am writing to you because of your company's involvement in this field and I hope that you will be able to answer the following questions that may help me with this project.	Say why you are writing to them in particular.
I am particularly interested in the following aspects: 1. Question 2. Question 3. Question	Do not ask them to solve your problem! Ask a few specific questions to which you believe they should reasonably be expected to know the answers. Do not ask commercially sensitive questions.
I would like to thank you in advance for your consideration and any information that you can give me. I enclose a stamped addressed envelope.	Thank them in advance and write again if they reply. Send a large SAE.
Yours faithfully *Rick Hancock* Rick Hancock	Sign the letter clearly.

I confirm that Rick Hancock is currently engaged on this project for his GCSE technology coursework and any assistance you could give him would be very much appreciated. Signed *Geoff Davis* Technology teacher	Ask your teacher to countersign the letter as this can increase your chances of a reply.

Fig. 2.14 Writing letters

2.8 Generating initial ideas

In order to produce ideas that will meet the specification you must produce a wide range of alternative solutions. Each of these must be compared with the specification in order to identify the most promising for further development.

Points to remember:

- produce a wide range of ideas by sketching – ideas are more important at this stage than technical accuracy
- evaluate your ideas with respect to the specification in note form
- explain why you have continued with some ideas and rejected others

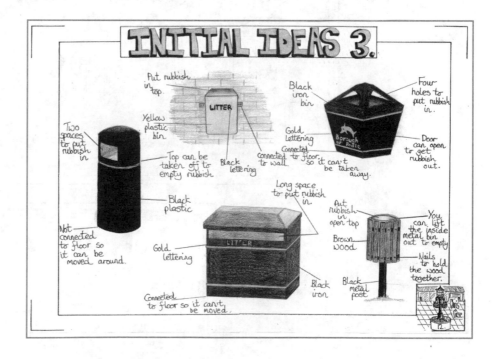

Fig. 2.14 Examples of sketched initial ideas

2.9 Development of the solution: modelling and prototypes

This involves a clearly reasoned development of an accepted idea into a final solution. The proposal must be modified progressively to ensure a sound solution when viewed against the specification.

Points to remember :

- test ideas as mock-ups as you go along using modelling materials (see Unit 5.7. for more information about modelling)
- seek the opinions of clients/experts/potential users
- draw upon earlier research to aid decisions on materials and manufacturing methods
- consider the social, environmental and health and safety aspects of the design
- sketching should now give way to more detailed forms of drawing
- the solution should be presented as a working drawing

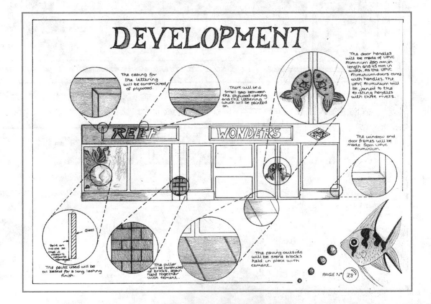

Fig.2.15 Examples of ideas being developed

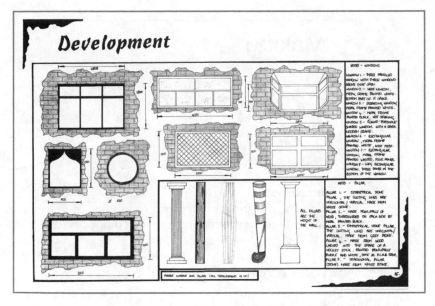

Fig. 2.15 Examples of ideas being developed (continued)

2.10 Planning for production

This involves consideration of all the necessary tools, materials and processes required to produce a high-quality product safely. Consideration must be given to the form in which the materials are produced for manufacture in industry and take account of the implications for your own design.

When producing a planning schedule, you must identify:

- each distinct stage in the manufacturing process in consecutive order
- the time available for each stage
- the tools, techniques, equipment and machinery needed
- ways of ensuring quality control
- health and safety issues

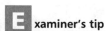
E **xaminer's tip**

Although a successful outcome may indicate adequate planning, it is essential that you present evidence in the form of a detailed planning schedule which records any decisions or modifications made.

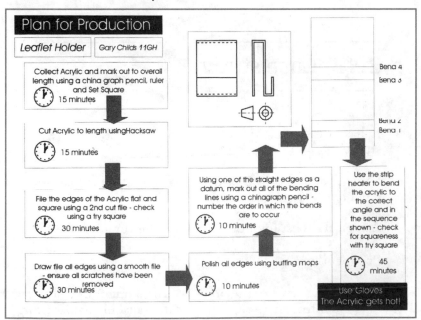

Fig. 2.16 Example of a planning schedule used for part of a project

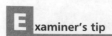
2.11 Making

This is the culmination of your project and as such must be given the time needed to ensure a quality outcome.

Points to remember:

- practise new skills first
- carry out test pieces to ensure suitability of material and process
- make adequate provision to store your work safely
- seek advice at every stage

See Fig. 2.17 for examples of completed coursework.

2.12 Testing and evaluation

You will have evaluated your project as an on-going excercise and at various stages. Each time you will have given reasons for how you have proceeded. You must now critically analyse your outcome in relation to your brief and specification, along with any issues arising from the making. It is also advisable to include comments on possible further developments – as this is naturally one of the last activities carried out, it is often poorly done, resulting in an unnecessary loss of marks.

Points to remember:

- for each of the specification bullet points, produce an evaluation point
- be critical
- suggest modifications and improvements
- test the solution in its intended setting
- seek the opinions of others

2.13 Case study

It has already been noted that a good method of research is to carry out a case study.

Some Examination Boards actually require a case study as a discrete assessed component (see pages 5–10)

A typical case study would contain some or all of the following elements:

Product details

- the name of the product, which might include a picture
- information regarding cost, availability, advertising
- an explanation of its function, including such aspects as safety and hygiene

Fig. 2.17 Examples of completed coursework artefacts

Visual analysis

- an annotated sketch of the product
- an exploded pictorial
- detailed drawings of significant parts

Materials analysis

- details of the raw materials and parts used
- possible reasons for the choice of these materials and parts
- details of finishes used

Production analysis

- details about how the product and its parts are manufactured
- possible reasons why these methods were chosen

Marketing analysis

- details of how the product is marketed
- discussion about the intended market
- comparison with similar products on the market

Evaluation

- a critical analysis of the product, commenting on issues such as aesthetics, ease of use, safety, durability, environmental considerations, value for money

Examiner's tip

A Case Study is an appropriate method of ensuring coverage of industrial practices.

Chapter 3
Electronic Products

3.1 Basic concepts

The five basic units within this course are the volt, the amp, the ohm, the watt and the farad.

The volt is the unit of electrical pressure. It is the difference in potential between the positive and negative terminals of the power source. The higher the voltage the greater is the force acting to cause current to flow in a given circuit.

The amp is the unit of current, that means the **rate** at which electricity flows around a circuit. The higher the current the 'faster' the current flows through a circuit. In most circuits, the amp is far too large a unit and the **milliamp** (one thousandth of an amp) is used.

The ohm is the unit of resistance. All materials (except superconductors) oppose the flow of electricity. Materials that have a very high resistance are called **insulators**, materials that have a very low resistance are called **conductors**. Copper is the most common conductor, because it has a very low resistance.

The watt is the unit of power which in electronics is the voltage × current (**Power = I**(amps) × Volts). Like the amp, the watt is usually too large a unit to be used in microelectronics. The **milliwatt** (one thousandth of a watt) is most commonly used.

The farad is the unit of capacitance which is the amount of electrical charge that can be stored in a capacitor.

Unit symbols

Volt = V
Amp = A
Ohm = Ω (the Greek capital letter omega)
Watt = W
Farad = F

E **xaminer's tip**

Three other symbols are commonly used:
Current = I
Resistance = R
Power = P

For most purposes these units are too large for use in low-power electronic circuits. The following symbols and prefixes are used:

Symbol	Prefix	Multiplier	
M	mega	one million	10^6
k	kilo	one thousand	10^3
m	milli	one thousandth	10^{-3}
μ	micro	one millionth	10^{-6}
n	nano	one thousand millionth	10^{-9}
p	pico	one million millionth	10^{-12}

Examples:

$2M2\Omega$ = 2.2 megaohms = 2.2 million ohms

$4k7\Omega$ = 4.7 kilohms = 4 thousand 7 hundred ohms

$75mA$ = 75 milliamps = $\dfrac{75}{1000}$ amps = 0.075 amps

$22\mu F$ = 22 microfarads = $\dfrac{22}{1\,000\,000}$ farads = 0.000 022 farads

$7nA$ = 7 nanoamps = $\dfrac{7}{1\,000\,000\,000}$ amps = 0.000 000 007 amps

$33pf$ = 33 picofarads = $\dfrac{33}{1\,000\,000\,000\,000}$ farads = 0.000 000 000 033 farads

3.2 Basic components

Power supplies

The power for most electronic circuits comes from batteries. There are basically two types of battery: dry and rechargeable.

Dry batteries

The basic single cell voltage of a dry battery is 1.5 volts (Fig. 3.1(a)), higher voltages can be achieved by connecting them together in series (Fig 3.1(b)).

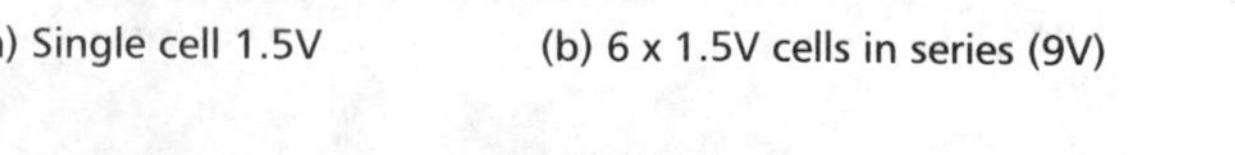

(a) Single cell 1.5V   (b) 6 x 1.5V cells in series (9V)

Fig. 3.1

Advantage: portable, can be used to power equipment which is remote from mains power.

Disadvantage: expensive, must be thrown away when exhausted.

Rechargeable batteries

There are two types of rechargeable cell: **wet** and **dry** cells. The most common example of a wet cell is the lead acid battery used in a car. The wet cell battery provides 2.0 volts per cell.

The most commonly used dry cell rechargeable battery is the nickel cadmium cell. This provides only 1.25 volts per cell.

Rechargeable batteries are initially more expensive but their low recharging costs and long life soon make them more economic than dry non-rechargeables.

3.3 Resistors

Resistors resist the flow of electricity through a circuit, i.e. they reduce the amount of current. Resistors can have a fixed value or be variable (known as potentiometers). The value of a resistor (in ohms) is indicated by a set of coloured bands on the body of the resistor.

Resistor colour code (Fig. 3.2)

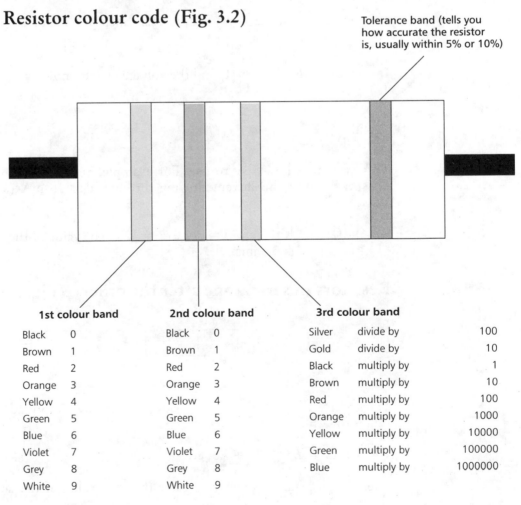

Tolerance band (tells you how accurate the resistor is, usually within 5% or 10%)

1st colour band		2nd colour band		3rd colour band		
Black	0	Black	0	Silver	divide by	100
Brown	1	Brown	1	Gold	divide by	10
Red	2	Red	2	Black	multiply by	1
Orange	3	Orange	3	Brown	multiply by	10
Yellow	4	Yellow	4	Red	multiply by	100
Green	5	Green	5	Orange	multiply by	1000
Blue	6	Blue	6	Yellow	multiply by	10000
Violet	7	Violet	7	Green	multiply by	100000
Grey	8	Grey	8	Blue	multiply by	1000000
White	9	White	9			

Fig. 3.2 Resistor colour code

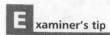
Examples

• Red – Red – Red	2 – 2 – x 100 (00)	=2,200 ohms or 2k2
• yellow – violet – brown	4 – 7 – x 10	=470 ohms
• brown – black – black	1 – 0 – x 1	=10 ohms
• green – blue – orange	5 – 6 – x 1,000	=56,000 ohms or 56k

Ohm's law

Ohm's law is a very important principle to learn. It defines the relationship between the voltage (V), the current (I), and the resistance (R).

Simply stated: **Voltage = I** (current) **x Resistance.**
The easiest way to remember this formula and rearrange it is to use the magic triangle. The magic triangle makes it easy to find the missing unit.

Examples

If you know the current (I) and the resistance (R), then V = I × R

If you know the voltage (V) and the resistance (R), then $I = \dfrac{V}{R}$

If you know the current (I) and the voltage (V), then $R = \dfrac{V}{I}$

This system is now easy to use. For example, an LED in a 6V circuit requires a resistor to limit the current flowing through it to 15 mA (0.015A). What value resistor is needed?

R = V/I   R therefore = 6/0.015 = 400 (The value of the required resistor is 400 ohms.)

Resistors in series (one after the other) (Fig. 3.3)

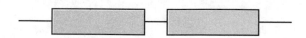

Fig. 3.3 Resistors in series

The total value of resistors in series is found by simply adding all the separate values together:

Rtotal = $R1 + R2 + R3$, etc.

The total resistance is always greater than the value of the largest resistor in the chain.

Resistors in parallel (side by side) - Fig. 3.4

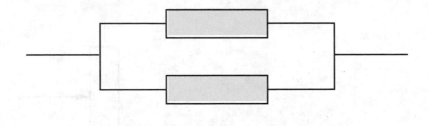

Fig. 3.4 Resistors in parallel

In order to work out the total of resistors in parallel you have to use reciprocals. The reciprocal of the total resistance is equal to the sum of the reciprocals of the individual resistors.

Example

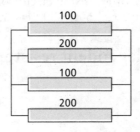

Fig. 3.5

Total resistance =

$$\frac{1}{R\text{total}} = \frac{1}{R1} + \frac{1}{R2} + \frac{1}{R3} + \frac{1}{R4}$$

Therefore:

$$\frac{1}{R\text{total}} = \frac{1}{100} + \frac{1}{200} + \frac{1}{100} + \frac{1}{200}$$

Find the common dominator i.e. (400)

$$\frac{1}{R\text{total}} = \frac{4}{400} + \frac{2}{400} + \frac{4}{400} + \frac{2}{400}$$

Add values together

$$\frac{1}{R\text{total}} = \frac{12}{400}$$

Turn reciprocals

$$\frac{R\text{total}}{1} = \frac{400}{12} \qquad \text{Therefore } R\text{total} = \frac{400}{12} = 33.3 \text{ ohms}$$

Variable resistors

These are known as potentiometers or pots for short (Fig. 3.6).

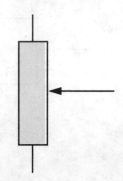

Fig.3.6 Variable resistor symbol

They vary in resistance as a knob is turned and are often used for changing the sensitivity of a sensing circuit or reducing the feedback to an amplifier, i.e. volume control on a radio or CD player.

Light dependent resistor (LDR)

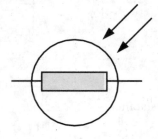

Fig.3.7 Light dependent resistor

LDRs are special resistors whose resistance changes according to the level of light which falls on their surface. The resistance can change from 10M ohms in the dark to about 1k ohms in bright light. This makes them ideal as light sensors for switching circuits.

Thermistor

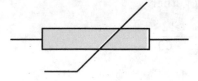

Fig.3.8 Thermistor

Thermistors are special resistors whose resistance changes according to the temperature (Fig. 3.8). This makes them ideal as temperature sensors.

3.4 Capacitors

(a) Fixed electrolytic capacitor symbol   (b) Fixed non-electrolytic capacitor symbol

Fig. 3.9

A capacitor is a device which is able to store electrical energy. When a capacitor is connected across a DC voltage supply with a current limiting series resistor it will charge up to the supply voltage in a short period of time. Once a capacitor is charged, the current leaks away slowly. It is this ability to charge and discharge which makes the capacitor a basic component in electronic timing circuits. There are three types:

- *variable* – not very common, used mainly for tuning radio circuits
- *fixed electrolytic* (fig. 3.9(a)) – a fixed value which has positive and negative terminals. This type must be connected the right way round otherwise it will blow.
- *fixed non-electrolytic* (Fig. 3.9(b)) – can be connected any way round

The unit of capacitance is the farad. As this is usually too large for use in microelectronic circuits, much smaller values are used (see page 44).

3.5 Switches

Switches are mechanical devices that can make (connect) or break (disconnect) a circuit. Switches can have different numbers of poles and throws. Poles are the number of connections they can make and throws are the number of positions to which each pole can be switched (Fig. 3.10).

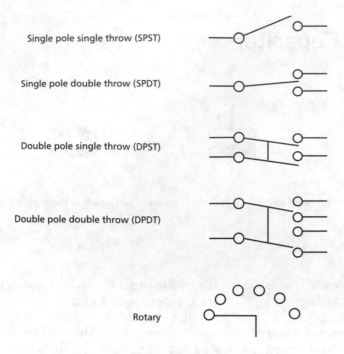

Single pole single throw (SPST)

Single pole double throw (SPDT)

Double pole single throw (DPST)

Double pole double throw (DPDT)

Rotary

Fig. 3.10 Switch types

Switch types

- Toggle: This type is very common – they normally have only two positions and are used as on/off switches.
- Slide: These can be found in low voltage circuits. They are used to set alternative positions, e.g. the MW/LW/FM switch on a radio.
- Push: (Fig. 3.11) These are push button switches which have a spring in them to return them when the pressure is released. There are two main types: **push to make** (connect the circuit) and **push to break** (disconnect the circuit).

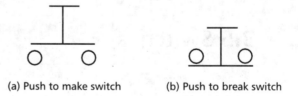

(a) Push to make switch   (b) Push to break switch

Fig. 3.11

- Rotary: These switches usually have 12 positions, each one equal to 30° rotation. There are different switching patterns available: 1 pole 12 way, 3 pole 4 way, 2 pole 6 way, 4 pole 3 way.

3.6 Diodes

Diodes are semiconductor devices which only allow the current to flow in one direction. There are two ways of connecting a diode in a circuit: forward biasing or reverse biasing. Forward biasing means that the diode is connected the 'right way round', i.e. with the positive side (anode) connected to the positive supply (Fig. 3.12(b)). When forward biased a diode will conduct. With reverse biasing the diode is connected the 'wrong way round' i.e. with the negative side (cathode) connected to the positive supply (Fig. 3.12(c)). When reverse biased, a diode will not conduct.

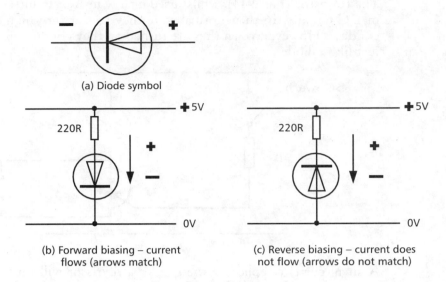

(a) Diode symbol

(b) Forward biasing – current
flows (arrows match)

(c) Reverse biasing – current does
not flow (arrows do not match)

Fig. 3.12

The light emitting diode (LED)

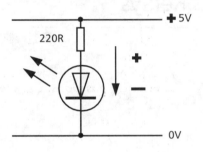

Fig. 3.13

This type of diode gives off light when current flows through it in the right direction (called forward biasing). LEDs can only take a small current, usually 20mA maximum otherwise they will be damaged. For this reason they should always be used with a current limiting resistor. Fig. 3.13 shows a LED with a current limiting resistor in series.

3.7 Thyristors (silicon controlled rectifiers)

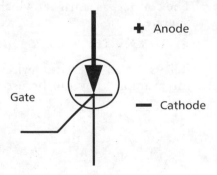

Fig. 3.14 Thyristor symbol

The thyristor (Fig. 3.14), whilst used mainly in AC circuits, can be useful as a latch in DC circuits. In their normal state they have a very high resistance and do not conduct. However, when they are turned on they conduct in the forward direction, just like a diode.

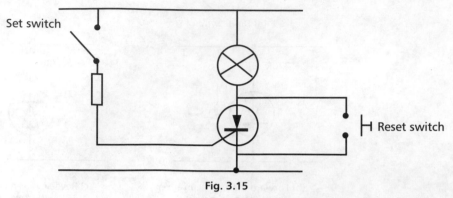

Fig. 3.15

A small current applied to the gate of a thyristor will cause it to conduct. It will remain 'latched' in this position until the current flowing through it is reduced to a certain minimum. In the circuit in Fig. 3.15 a reset switch is added for this purpose.

3.8 Relays

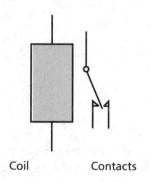

Coil   Contacts

Fig. 3.16

A relay (Fig 3.16) is an **electromechanical** device consisting of two parts: the coil and the contacts. When current passes through the coil it creates a magnetic field. The coil acts as a magnet which attracts the contacts of the the switch, causing it to operate.

Relays are an interface device – this means that they link one system to another, for example they can be used in a battery-operated circuit to switch to mains voltage.

3.9 Integrated circuits (ICs)

Fig. 3.17 Integrated circuits

Integrated circuits (Fig. 3.17) are small electronic circuits that have many different components built onto a small slice of silicon (semiconductor). The integrated circuits are housed in a plastic case. They are usually in a DIL (dual in line) configuration. Dual in line simply means two sets of parallel connections (pins). Pin number 1 is usually identified with a small circle and with the IC held upright the remaining pins are numbered anticlockwise (Fig. 3.18).

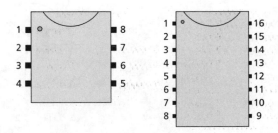

Fig. 3.18 IC pin numbers

3.10 Transistors

Transistors are three-lead current-operated devices that can provide amplification (i.e. the output current is greater than the input current. The amount by which a transistor amplifies current is called **gain** (hFe) of the transistor. The three leads are called the **base**, the **emitter** and the **collector**.

There are two main types of transistor, the n–p–n and the p–n–p. As can be seen in Fig.3.19 in the n–p–n transistor the arrow points away from the base and in the p–n–p it points towards the base. The arrow always points to the negative supply.

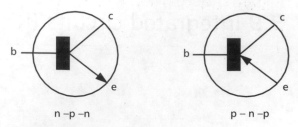

Fig. 3.19

Identifying the leads

The most common transistor layouts looking from underneath are shown in Fig. 3.20.

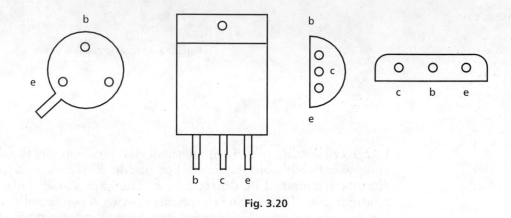

Fig. 3.20

The transistor as a current amplifier (Fig. 3.21)

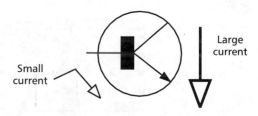

Fig. 3.21

When a small current flows through the base emitter circuit, a much larger (amplified) current flows through the collector emitter circuit. This type of arrangement is useful in sensing circuits, e.g. when a small current from a light sensor switches a relay to turn on the mains electricity for an automatic porch light. As can be seen, both the emitter current (Ie) and the collector current (Ic) flow through the emitter. This is shown by the formula Ie = Ic + Ie.

The voltage to the base of the transistor is fed through a current limiting resistor. A minimum of 0.6V is needed before the transistor will begin to switch; this is called the threshold voltage.

Transistor gain (hFe)

The current flowing into the base of the transistor is much smaller than the current flowing from the collector to the emitter. The ratio of the collector current, Ic, to the base current, Ib, is called the **gain** (hFe).

Calculating the base current

In the circuit shown in Fig. 3.22 a collector current of 50mA is needed for the bulb to light. The gain (hFe) of the transistor is 200. What is the required base current?

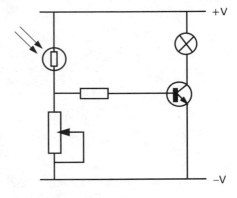

Ic = Ib × hFe therefore

0.050 = Ib × 200

therefore:

Ib = 0.050 / 200 = 0.00025A

(0.25mA)

Fig. 3.22

Transistor power

The power of a transistor is related to the collector current that can pass before the transistor overheats and stops working. The power rating must not be exceeded.

The transistor as a switch

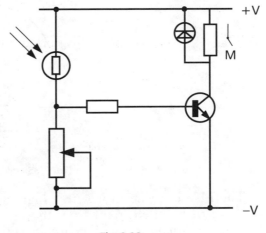

Fig. 3.23

The transistor is often used as a switch which swings from an 'off' position to a fully 'open' position when a base current is applied. This is very useful in sensing circuits as shown in Fig. 3.23. In this circuit, as the light level reaches a certain point, the relay will switch on completely.

Making the transistor arrangement more sensitive (increasing the amplification)

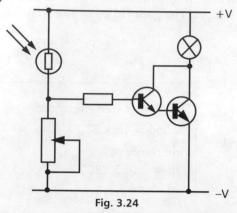

Fig. 3.24

The most common way of doing this is to use the **Darlington pair** arrangement. The Darlington pair uses two transistors connected together. In Fig. 3.24 a BC180 (gain about 180) is paired with a BFY51 power transistor (gain about 50). The resultant gain is now equal to 180 x 50 or 9000 and means that the higher collector current can be triggered by a very low base current. This arrangement acts like a single transistor with a very high gain *and* a high output current.

The field effect transistor (FET) - Fig. 3.25

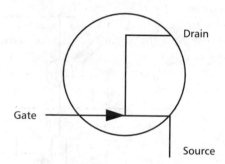

Fig. 3.25 Field effect transistor

The FET is a transistor with a high input impedance (resistance) which means it draws very little current from the signal source. It is often used in radio circuits. FETs are used for amplifier circuits with small gains but a large input impedance.

3.11 Timing circuits

Creating time delays

The resistor and capacitor are the basis of most timer circuits (often referred to as RC circuits). As we have already seen, a capacitor is a device which can store electricity. The time it takes to charge up (and discharge) is determined by its own size and the size of the resistor used with it. The time taken to charge a capacitor to two-thirds of the supply voltage is called the **time constant**.

The time constant can be calculated by: $t(\text{seconds}) = C(\text{farads}) \times R(\text{ohms})$

The 555 timer IC

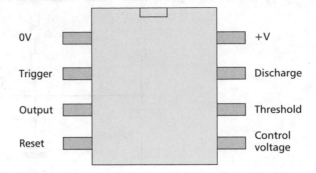

Fig. 3.26 555 timer IC

Although timing circuits can be developed using discrete components (resistors, capacitors, etc.) it is usual to use the 555 timer IC (Fig. 3.26). The 555 comes in an 8-pin DIL pack and is very cheap to buy. One of its main advantages is that it can be used both as an astable or monostable timer.

The monostable timer

The monostable circuit (Fig. 3.27) is one which has only one stable state – this means that it remains off (logic 0) until triggered. When a positive voltage (0V–5V) is applied to the trigger the output goes high (logic 1) for a time determined by the values of the resistors and capacitors used. At the end of the time period it returns to its original state until once again triggered. This makes it ideal for a device such as a burglar alarm which once triggered will sound for a set time.

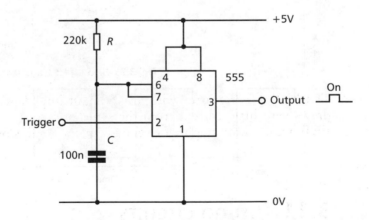

Fig. 3.20 The NE555 in a monostable configuration

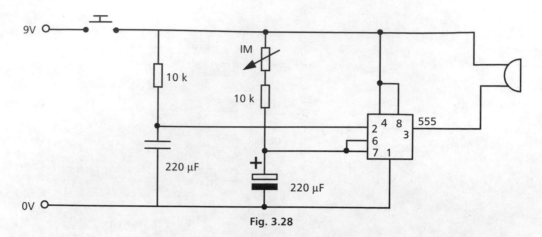

Fig. 3.28

Notice that with the egg timer, the buzzer (Fig. 3.28) is connected from the supply to the output of the 555. In this configuration the 555 is acting as a 'sink' rather than a source; this means that the buzzer works when the output of the 555 is low (i.e. 0V) rather than high. The 555 'sinks' much more current than it is able to 'source'. In order to operate a buzzer when used as a source, an amplifier stage would be needed..

The astable timer

The astable circuit has **no** stable output – this means that it continually switches from high output (logic 1) to low output (logic 0) – depicted in graph in Fig. 3.29. The astable generates a pulse, the time period of which is determined by the value of the resistors and capacitors used. Because it generates a pulse it is used as a clock in timing circuits.

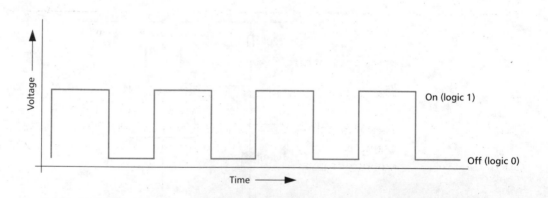

Fig. 3.29

Two examples of astable circuits are shown in Figs 3.30 and 3.31.

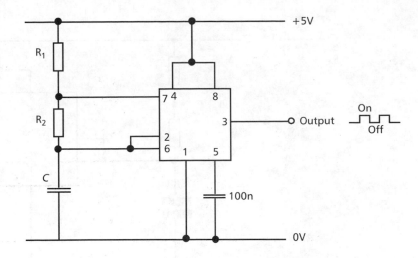

Fig. 3.30 555 astable configuration

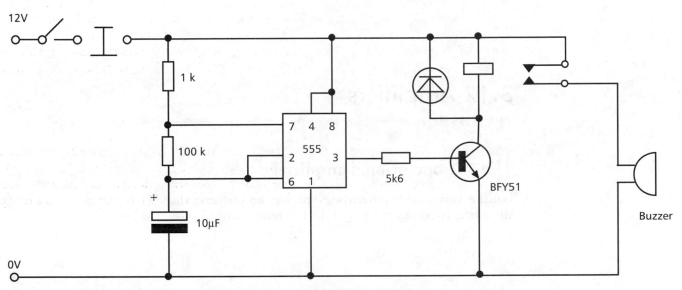

Fig. 3.31 Car reversing alarm

Frequency of an astable timer

The frequency of an astable is the number of changes (or cycles) in one second. The unit of frequency is the Hertz (Hz). One repetition every second (such as a normal watch or clock) is a frequency of 1Hz. The clock speed of computers, for example, is very fast; new PCs have clock frequencies of 200 MHz (200,000,000 repetitions per second!).

Calculating the frequency of an astable timer (Fig. 3.32)

$$f\,(\mathrm{Hz}) = \frac{1.44}{(R1+2R2)\,C}$$

Therefore

$$f = \frac{1.44}{(0.001+0.200)\ \mathrm{x}\ 10}$$

$$f = \frac{1.44}{2.01}$$

$$f = 0.7\,\mathrm{Hz\ (approx.)}$$

Units: R in Mega ohms
C in μF

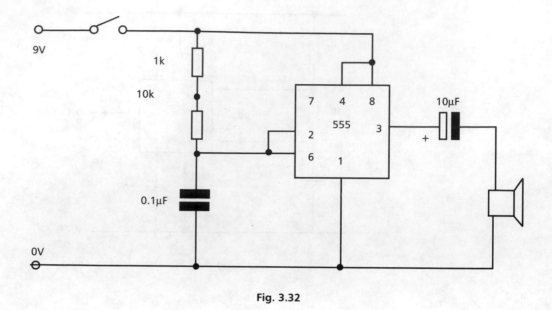

Fig. 3.32

3.12 Amplifiers

The 741 operational amplifier

Unlike transistors which are current amplifiers, the 741 op amp is a **voltage** amplifier. It comes in an 8-pin DIL arrangement as shown in Fig. 3.33.

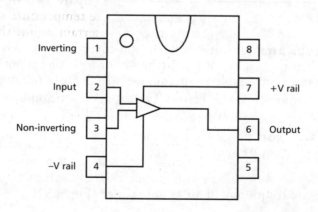

Fig. 3.33 741 pin connections

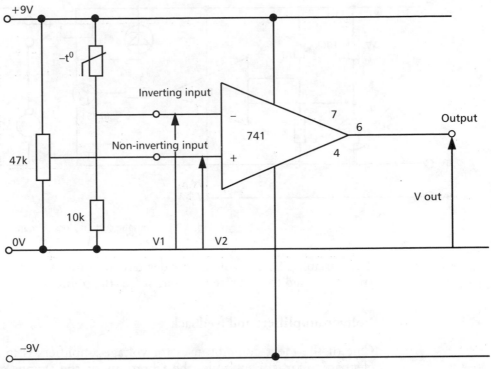

Fig. 3.34 741 circuit diagram

Features:

- has a gain of approximately 100,000
- uses a split power supply (requires a positive voltage, a negative voltage and a 0V supply)
- has an inverting and a non-inverting input

The 741 as comparator

When used as a comparator, the 741 will compare two inputs and amplify the difference. This is very good for sensing. In the temperature sensing circuit shown in Fig.3.34, when the temperature rises to a certain point, the output will swing. When the voltage at pin 3 (the +ve or non-inverting input) is higher, the output is positive. When the voltage at pin 2 (the –ve or inverting input) is higher the output is negative. Because the gain is so large (100,000) the tiniest difference in voltage will cause the output to go fully on. In fact the op amp will saturate if the difference of the two inputs is greater than 0.004 mV.

The 741 op amp has a high impedance (internal resistance) therefore it will only source or sink about 10mA. Because of this it needs a power transistor connected to the output in order to power output devices such as a motor, lamp or heater (Fig. 3.35).

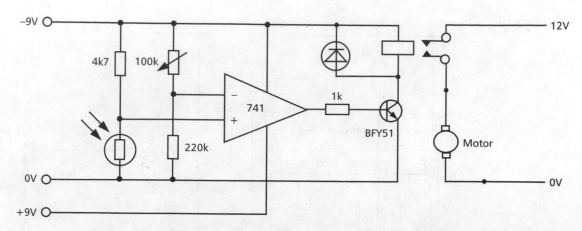

Fig. 3.35 Automatic curtain closer circuit

The variable resistor voltage divider circuit connected to the non-inverting input (pin 2) is used to calibrate the system (set the point at which the system switches).

Voltage amplifiers and feedback

One of the most common uses for voltage amplifiers is in audio systems. On an electric guitar, for example, the vibrations of the strings are converted to small electrical signals by the transducers (pickups). These signals need to be amplified in order to be heard and because of the very high gain (almost infinite) of the op amp, some of the output must be fed back into the input in order to control its magnitude – this is called **feedback**.

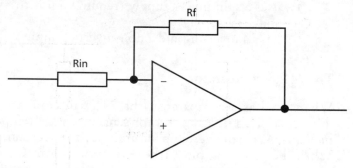

Fig. 3.36 The basic op amp feedback configuration using the inverting input

If we assume that the op amp has infinite gain, the gain is controlled only by the value of Rf (the feedback resistor) and Rin (the input resistor).

The voltage gain therefore of an **inverting amp** $= \dfrac{Rf}{Rin}$

A practical inverting amplifier circuit - Fig. 3.37

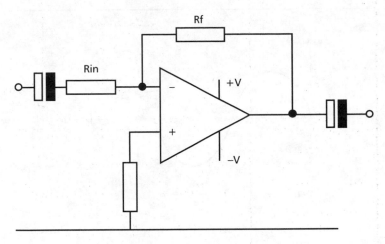

Fig. 3.37 Practical inverting amplifier circuit

Note The capacitors are called de-coupling capacitors and are used in AC circuits to ensure that no DC passes into the circuit and is amplified – this would lead to distortion. AC passes through a capacitor but DC does not. These are not needed in DC circuits.

A practical non-inverting amplifier circuit - Fig. 3.38

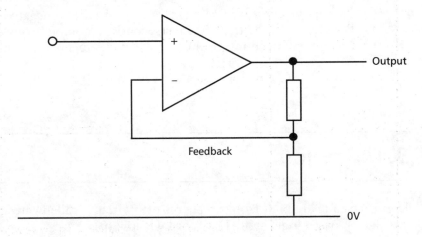

Fig. 3.38 Practical non-inverting amplifier circuit

Note Although the input is applied to the non–inverting input, the feedback is applied to the inverting input.

The gain of the non-inverting amplifier is: $\dfrac{Rin + Rf}{Rin}$

Summary

- an inverting amplifier magnifies the voltage and changes its polarity
- a non-inverting amplifier magnifies the voltage but does not change the polarity
- feedback is essential in order to control the output.

3.13 Alternating current (AC)

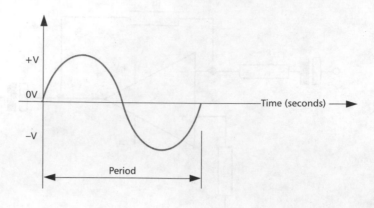

Fig. 3.39

An alternating current supply is one that alternates from positive to negative at regular intervals. Mains electricity for example is supplied at 240v, 50 Hz, – it alternates from positive to negative 50 times a second.

The three important properties to know are

- Cycle: one cycle is a complete set of positive and negative values
- Period: this is the time taken in seconds to complete one cycle
- Frequency: the number of complete cycles in a one second period (*t* secs)

The shape of the AC waveform is called a sinewave (Fig. 3.39)

3.14 Logic

Digital circuits are built from simple on/off switches, called gates. These gates have **two** states: on or logic high (1), off or logic low (0).

Logic tables or **truth tables** can be produced to analyse clearly the possible alternative states of a digital circuit. For example, in the simple circuit in Fig. 3.40, the output will only be high (logic 1) when switches A and B are on.

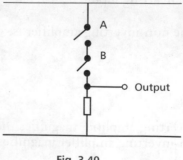

Fig. 3.40

The truth table for this circuit is called an AND gate.

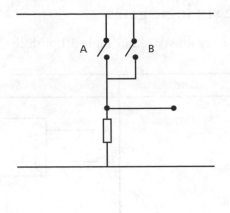

Fig. 3.41

In the digital circuit in Fig. 3.41 the output will go high (logic 1) if either switch A or B is closed.

The truth table for this circuit is called an OR gate

All logic circuits can be made from switches connected together in order to achieve desired output states. In all there are six types of logic gates used.

The six logic gates

These are illustrated in Table 3.1 with their respective truth tables.

Gate	Symbol	Truth table
AND	A — Output, B	A B Output 0 0 0 1 0 0 0 1 0 1 1 1
OR	A — Output, B	A B Output 0 0 0 1 0 1 0 1 1 1 1 1
NOT (or inverter)	A — Output	A Output 0 1 1 0
NAND (an inverted AND)	A — Output, B	A B Output 0 0 1 1 0 1 0 1 1 1 1 0
NOR (an inverted OR)	A — Output, B	A B Output 0 0 1 1 0 0 0 1 0 1 1 0
Exclusive OR (XOR)	A — Output, B	A B Output 0 0 0 1 0 1 0 1 1 1 1 0 (Only logic 1 when **either** input is 1 **not** when both)

Table 3.1

Logic families

There are two distinct logic families, transistor transistor logic (TTL) and complementary metal oxide semiconductor (CMOS) giving rise to two different types of integrated circuits. The TTL logic ICs are listed as the 7400 series and the CMOS ICs are listed as the 4000 B series. The main operating differences between these two logic families is given in Table 3.2.

Table 3.2

Property	TTL	CMOS
Power supply	5V (+/–0.25V)	3–15V
Current required	3mA	8μA
Input impedance	low	high
Temperature range	0–70	–40 to +85

When choosing logic ICs for particular output requirements, great care must be taken. Both TTL and CMOS ICs have limited current output. TTL ICs will source 8mA but can sink 16mA. Therefore, in order to light an LED (requiring say 10mA), the TTL IC should be used as a current sink. The CMOS IC will source only 0.02 mA and sink 8mA. An amplifier stage such as a Darlington pair will always need to be used to power output devices such as a motor.

Counting with logic circuits

The simplest counter is a bistable or flip flop. These can be built very simply using gates. The example in Fig. 3.42 uses Nor gates. The feedback latches the output in the state until the reset switch is pushed. This type of bistable is called an SR flip flop (standing for Set Reset)

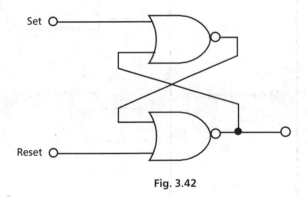

Fig. 3.42

SR flip flops are mainly used as simple latches; for example, they can be used to operate a solenoid bolt on a door using the circuit in Fig.3.43.

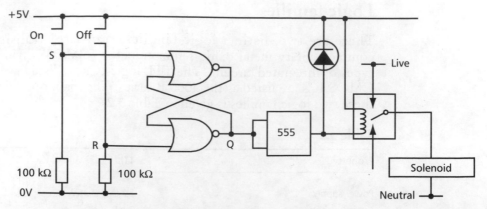

Fig. 3.43 Simple latch circuit

Pressing the set switch will operate the solenoid and hold it in the open position until the reset switch is pushed. However, this type of latch has one big drawback, there is no control over it when the set switch is pressed. An improved system would only allow the set signal to be changed at a particular time, this is called a clocked bistable. The D type flip flop is a clocked bistable (Fig. 3.44). The main advantage of the D type flip flop is that it is triggered by a rising edge (increasing voltage) rather than a complete pulse (0–1).

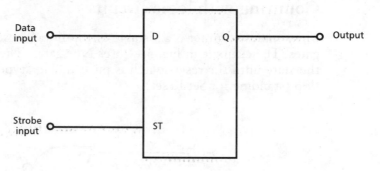

Fig. 3.44 D type flip flop

Using a D type flip flop, place the bit that you want to remember at the Data terminal. The strobe terminal is pulsed for an instant. The bit will be held at Q until the next time the ST is pulsed. A practical example is shown in Fig. 3.45.

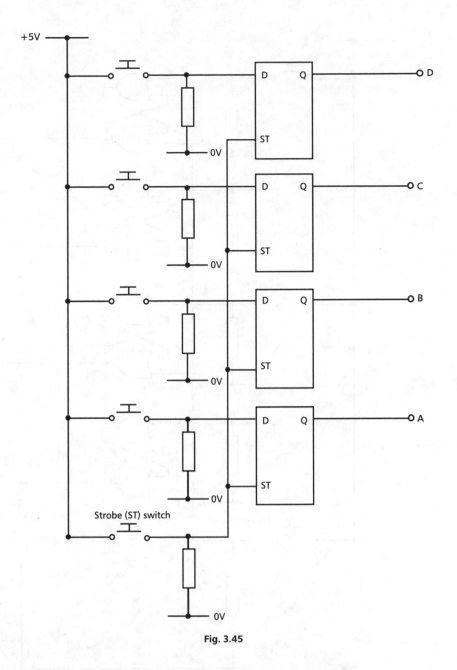

Fig. 3.45

The circuit shown in Fig. 3.45 uses four D type flip flops to count four people present at a particular time, for example a school register. At a time, say 9.15am, the students present press their switch, the teacher presses the ST at the same time. Only those present at the time the ST is pressed will be counted as present.

Displaying the output

When using a D type flip flop, one good way of displaying the output is to use an LED. The circuit in Fig. 3.46 shows how a 4-bit LED display could be used with D type flip flops.

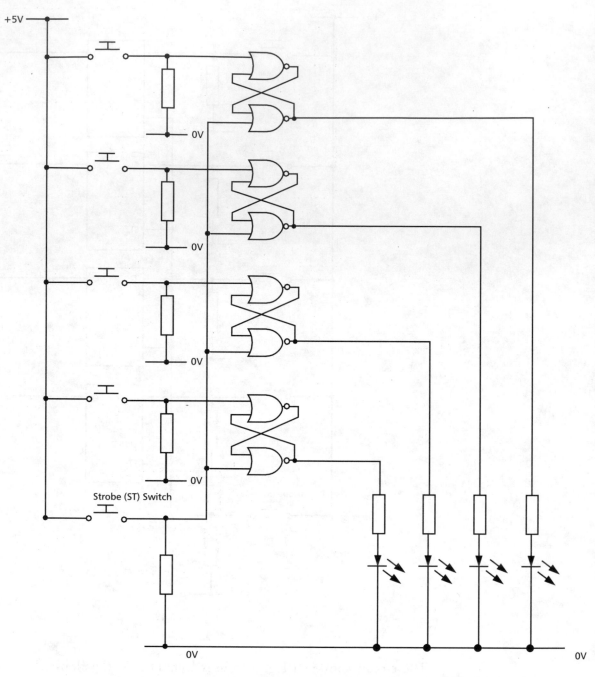

Fig. 3.46

Displaying numbers

The most common way to display numbers is to use seven segment displays. There are basically two types of display – the liquid crystal display (LCD) and the LED display. LCDs use virtually no current but work on reflected light and therefore will not work in the dark. LED displays draw relatively large amounts of current and will work in the dark.

Each segment of the display is identified by a lower-case letter (Fig. 3.47). Each segment can be switched on independently in order to create the numbers 0–9. The number 2 shown is created by using only the segments a, b, g, e, and d.

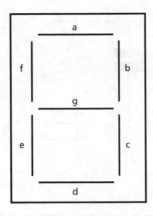 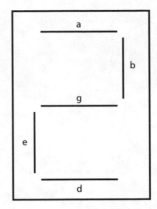

Fig 3.47

In order to convert the output from a counter into a number display, the binary output (a 'word' made up of zeros and ones) must be decoded. A binary coded decimal (BCD) chip is used. The BCD receives a binary code and coverts this to seven-segment display format.

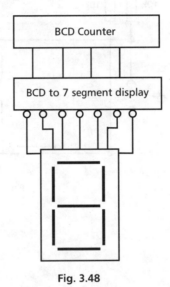

Fig. 3.48

The circuit in Fig 3.48 shows how the whole system might work.

It is very important when designing any counting circuits that a smooth signal comes from the input switch. Mechanical switches suffer from the problem of 'bounce'. That is, when they are pressed the contacts bounce off each other several times before they finally close. This will cause a multiple signal which will be taken as a series of pulses by the counting circuit. Switch debounce circuits are easy to construct. Two examples are given in Fig. 3.49.

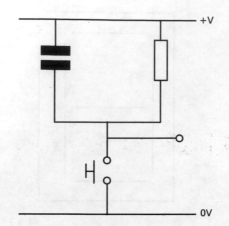

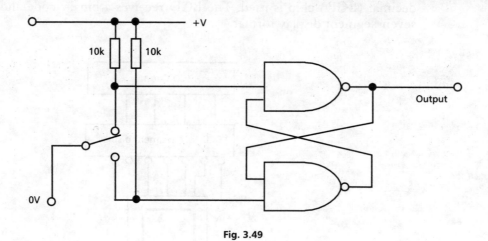

Fig. 3.49

Chapter 4
Food technology

4.1 Equipment

You will be expected to be able to select and use the following basic tools and equipment used in food preparation.

Equipment	Uses	Appearance
Teaspoon, dessertspoon and tablespoon	Used for measuring, mixing, tasting, serving and eating.	
Kitchen knives	Used for cutting and scraping. Stainless steel knives are best and must be kept sharp for safety reasons.	
Kitchen scissors	Used for cutting greaseproof paper and ingredients such as parsley, etc.	
Peelers and corers	More effective than knives for the less experienced.	Apple corer Potato peeler

Equipment	Uses	Appearance
Graters and choppers	Useful for smaller amounts of food and when a processor is not available. Require careful cleaning.	
Wooden spoon	Available in different shapes and sizes. Used for stirring, beating and blending.	
Hand whisk	Used on small quantities in order to add bulk.	
Rotary whisk	More convenient for larger quantities if an electric mixer is not available.	
Electric food mixer	Much quicker than the hand versions and essential for larger quantities.	
Food processor	Used for grating, slicing, mincing, mixing and kneading dough. The different attachments need thorough cleaning.	
Scales	Used for measuring the weight of ingredients. For smaller quantities, the more accurate spring-balance scales should be used.	

Equipment	Uses	Appearance
Measuring jug	Used for measuring the volume of liquids.	
Measuring spoons	Graduated spoons for measuring the volume of dry ingredients.	
Spatula and palette knife	Used for spreading or cleaning out bowls.	
Mixing bowls and basins	Made from earthenware, glass or plastic and coming in a wide range of sizes.	
Chopping board	Traditionally made from wood, but more hygienic if synthetic.	
Rolling pin and cutters	The basic equipment for biscuit and pastry making – used with a cutting board. Most effective when kept cool.	
Saucepans	Available in a wide range of sizes and materials. If provided, the lid should fit well. Can have oven-proof handles for use in the oven.	

Equipment	Uses	Appearance
Frying pan	Used for shallow frying with small amounts of fat or oil. Can be more effective when used with a lid. They are also produced with more rounded sides for the easier removal of omelettes, etc.	
Casserole dishes	Can be made of ceramic, glass or metal – the latter must not be used in a micro-wave.	
Microwave oven	Useful for rapid cooking of frozen and pre-prepared food. It should be serviced regularly for safety reasons.	
Deep fat fryer	Much safer than a large saucepan on a hob.	
Pressure cooker	Saves time and fuel when preparing stews, vegetables, etc.	

Equipment	Uses	Appearance
Conventional oven	Can be gas or electric and should be serviced regularly. Many are now fan assisted to create more uniform heating. They are an obvious safety hazard especially with hot saucepans on the hob or when removing items from the oven.	

Fig. 4.1 Food preparation tools and equipment

4.2 Nutrition

The food that the body consumes contains the fuel required to produce the energy needed to sustain it at work, rest and play. Food also contains elements that are not needed and can be actually detrimental to health. The components that are useful to the body are known as **nutrients**. They are classified in five different types and have different jobs within the body (see Fig. 4.2).

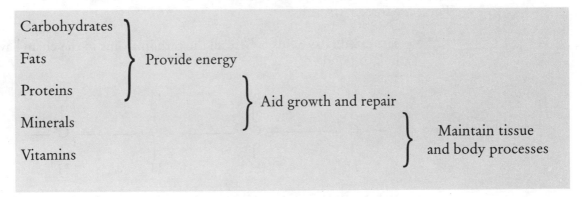

Fig. 4.2 Nutrient types

Carbohydrates

Carbohydrates are produced by plants through photosynthesis and contain three elements: carbon, hydrogen and oxygen.

The simplest forms are **monosaccharides**. These are sugars such as fructose, glucose and galactose which are absorbed into the body.

When photosynthesis continues, **disaccharides** are formed from two monosaccharides. Disaccharides such as sucrose, maltose and lactose are broken down by digestion into monosaccharides before being absorbed.

Further photosynthesis produces the third main group of carbohydrates, **polysaccharides**. The most common of these are the starches which, unlike sugars, are not soluble in water. These, again, have to be broken down into glucose during digestion.

The five main polysaccharides are:

- Starch – which forms the basis of most diets around the world with each area having its own staple diet, e.g. rice in Asia, potatoes in Europe and corn in South America.

- Dextrin – which is formed when starch foods are baked/toasted.

- Cellulose – which forms the roughage in our diet, being derived from plant cells.

- Pectin – which gels in water and therefore aids setting.

- Glycogen – which is stored in the liver having been formed during digestion. It is then converted to glucose.

Fats

Fats (including oils which generally remain liquid at room temperature) are needed by the body in far smaller quantities than carbohydrates and are obtained from milk, oily fish, meat, seeds and nuts. They are made up of the same three elements as carbohydrates and perform the similar functions of providing energy, insulation when stored and allowing vitamins to be transported.

The name for a fat is a **triglyceride**, which is formed from a molecule of **glycerol** and three chains of **fatty acids**.

There are three fatty acids:

- **saturated fatty acids**, where all the carbon atoms in the chain have a single link or bond

$$
\begin{array}{ccccccc}
& H & & H & & H & & H \\
& | & & | & & | & & | \\
-\!\!-\, & C & -\!\!-\!\!- & C & -\!\!-\!\!- & C & -\!\!-\!\!- & C & -\!\!- \\
& | & & | & & | & & | \\
& H & & H & & H & & H
\end{array}
$$

- **mono-unsaturated fatty acids**, where there is a single double bond in the chain, enabling it to take on more hydrogen atoms – it is not saturated.

$$
\begin{array}{ccccccc}
& H & & H & & H & & H \\
& & & & & | & & | \\
-\!\!-\, & C & =\!\!=\!\!= & C & -\!\!-\!\!- & C & -\!\!-\!\!- & C & -\!\!- \\
& & & & & | & & | \\
& & & & & H & & H
\end{array}
$$

- **poly-unsaturated fatty acids**, where there is more than one double bond and a greater capacity to take on hydrogen atoms.

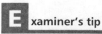

Most fats and oils contain saturated and unsaturated fatty acids. Animal fats contain higher percentages of saturated fatty acids, while vegetable oils are high in unsaturated fatty acids. This is critical for health reasons since saturated fats can increase the **cholesterol** level in the blood which can lead to heart disease if deposited on the walls of the arteries. Fats containing a high proportion of unsaturated fatty acids are softer at room temperature, having a lower melting point.

Proteins

Proteins are made up of the four elements carbon, hydrogen, oxygen and nitrogen, and sometimes sulphur and phosphorus in addition. These elements form chains of protein molecules called **amino-acids**. They are essential to life and can only be obtained from food.

Examiner's tip

You should emphasise that a variety of foods is the best way to ensure that the body has the correct amounts of essential amino-acids.

Adults require eight essential amino-acids, whilst children require a further two. Food containing all ten essential amino-acids are known as **high biological value proteins** (HBV); they are generally found in meat, fish, eggs and milk.

Plant foods such as pulses, nuts and cereals have one or more amino-acids absent and are known as **low biological value proteins** (LBV), but can supplement each other in combination. Soya beans, however, are HBV and form the basis of **textured vegetable protein** (TVP), a common meat substitute used by vegetarians.

Minerals

Minerals play an important part in forming and maintaining:

- the skeletal structure of the body, e.g.
  - **calcium** in milk, cheese
  - **phosphorus** in cheese, eggs, fish, meat
  - **magnesium**

- the soft tissues, e.g.
  - **potassium** in fruit and vegetables

- the body fluid, e.g.
  - **sodium** in salt
  - **chlorine**

Iron (liver, kidney, egg yolk) is needed for the replacement of red blood cells and, because of menstruation, women require more iron than men.

Small amounts of the trace elements **iodine** (seafood, milk, spinach) and **fluorine** (seafood, the water supply in many areas) are required for regulating the metabolic rate of the body and for hardening the enamel in teeth respectively.

Vitamins

Vitamins are found in small quantities in many foods and can be put in two groups:

- fat-soluble vitamins – A, D, E and K
- water soluble vitamins – B group and C

Vitamin A
- good for the eyesight, healthy skin and mucous membranes
- found in animal foods, oily fish and less effectively in fruit and vegetables

Vitamin D
- good for formation of bones and teeth
- found mainly in animal foods

Vitamin E
- found in eggs, cereal oils, liver and meat

Vitamin K
- stops bleeding by blood clotting
- found in green vegetables, fish, liver

Vitamin B1
- known as **Thiamin**, helps release the energy from carbohydrates and the functioning of the nervous system
- found in many foods, especially wholegrain cereals

Vitamin B2
- known as **Riboflavin**, helps release energy and therefore aids growth rate in children
- found in many animal products and yeast

Niacin
- or **Nicotinic acid**, again helps release energy
- found in many foods

Vitamin B12
- aids the metabolism of amino-acids
- found in animal foods only

Vitamin C
- or **Ascorbic acid**, makes connective tissue, aids the absorption of iron and assists the formation of bones and teeth
- found mainly in fruit and raw green vegetables

Examiner's tip

You should concentrate on the concept of a balanced diet providing the right amount of nutrients.

Fibre (roughage)

Dietary fibre is not digested and absorbed by the body, being mainly the outer husks and peel of plant food. However, it is important to the digestive system because it can absorb water and adds bulk, thus it helps to avoid constipation.

Water

Water is essential for life and is contained in fruit, juices, vegetables and milk. There is a constant requirement for water as it is lost through perspiration, breathing out and urine, which removes some of the body's waste products in solution.

Metabolism

The rate at which the body uses up energy is known as the **metabolic rate (MR)**. This rate varies depending on the height and weight of the person and on what they are doing. The rate at which the body uses energy to perform the basic tasks of remaining alive is known as the **basal metabolic rate (BMR)**.

For each person there are **recommended daily amounts (RDA)** of nutrients needed to support a healthy body.

4.3 Special dietary needs

Diet changes throughout the world through custom and availability. However, diet is also changed through necessity, e.g. medical reasons, or by choice, e.g. religion, personal beliefs.

The following are some of the dietary preferences that exist.

Diabetics
- must control carbohydrate intake by eating low fat, high-fibre foods

Pregnant women
- need a high calcium and iron intake
- need protein-rich food
- should consume more fresh fruit and vegetables
- should avoid alcohol

Vegetarians
- do not eat food that involves killing animals

Vegans
- avoid all animal products

Muslims
- do not eat pork or shellfish
- do not consume alcohol
- eat meat slaughtered and prepared in a special way
- fast on a regular basis

Hindus
- do not eat beef
- eat mostly vegetables
- do not consume alcohol

Jews
- do not eat pork
- eat only fish with scales and fins
- eat food prepared in a special way, especially for the festival of Passover
- do not eat milk and meat together

Rastafarians
- do not eat animal products except milk
- avoid canned or processed food
- do not consume salt, coffee or alcohol
- eat only organically grown food

4.4 Working properties

Aerating

Aeration is the addition of gas to make the food lighter in texture. This can be achieved in a number of ways:

- *whisking*, which adds air to such ingredients as eggs
- *adding raising agents*, such as yeast, which adds carbon dioxide
- *adding liquid*, such as milk, which produces steam during cooking

Binding

Some ingredients will not bind together when mixed and require another ingredient to aid this. Ingredients commonly used include water, eggs, fats and flour.

Bulking

In some recipes, one ingredient will be used as the main part to fill it out. Examples are flour in bread and rice in risotto.

Browning

Browning is a change of colour in food and can be both attractive and unattractive to the consumer. There are four basic causes of browning.

1 **Non-enzymatic browning** This is the reaction of carbohydrate and a protein, producing flavour, aroma and a brown colour. The outside of meat does this during cooking and is generally considered appetising, which is why grills are added to microwave ovens to achieve the effect.

2 **Caramelisation** This happens when sugar is heated above its melting point and turns brown producing a pleasant flavour. Care must be taken not to over heat it or it will turn black and be bitter to taste.

3 **Enzymic browning** This occurs when some fruits, e.g. apples, bananas and pears, are cut and left exposed to the air, turning them brown as the oxygen reacts with them. It can be avoided by heating, adding a hot syrup, adding an acid like lemon juice or blanching.

4 **Dextrinisation** This is the browning that occurs when starch turns to dextrin during cooking, e.g. bread, toast and cakes.

Colouring

The colour of food can be unappetising, especially if it is not the colour expected. Ingredients will often change colour when processed or cooked and so colouring agents are added to enhance or return the colour to its original. These additives are not liked by some as they are not necessary for nutrition or taste, and in some cases have been linked with allergic reactions.

Emulsifying

Emulsifiers allow other liquids such as fats and oils to mix together in an emulsion and produce a smooth product. Beating will assist this process as it increases the surface area of each component. Egg and mustard can be used as emulsifiers in mayonnaise.

Flavouring

Flavour is a combination of taste and smell and therefore can be affected if someone has a cold or smokes. Flavour can be lost in processing and so flavourings are sometimes added to restore or enhance the taste.

They are classified as natural, nature identical or artificial. Monosodium glutamate is a commonly used flavour enhancer. Once again, it is not liked by everybody, and natural herbs, spices and seasonings are often preferred.

Moistening

Some foods will be naturally dry and therefore less palatable. The addition of liquids or ingredients containing more moisture will alleviate this.

Preserving

Food can suffer deterioration caused by bacteria, fungi and moulds. Preservatives can increase the length of time food can be stored. Sugar in jam preserves the fruit, whilst vinegar will preserve the vegetables in pickles and salt can preserve fish.

Setting

Eggs, gelatine, cornflour are all used to set jellies and cold sauces.

Shortening

Shortening is the addition of fats and oils to flour in order to achieve a crisp and crumbly texture.

Stabilising

Stabilisers, such as starch and egg white, keep an emulsion stable by forming a gel which makes it more difficult for the components to separate. The smaller the particles in the emulsion, the more likely they are to stay together. Without the use of a stabiliser emulsions are likely to separate to some extent with time.

Examiner's tip

Concentrate on the reduction of added sugar during processing which provides energy but has little nutritional value and encourages tooth decay.

Sweetening

Many foods such as fruit and honey can sweeten dishes, but the main one used is sugar. Artificial sweeteners such as saccharin and aspartame can also be used. These are much sweeter than sugar and so less is used. They are also lower in calories and are used to reduce sugar consumption on health grounds. Once again, however, there are concerns about reactions and side effects.

Adding texture

A dish having only one texture can be dull and so the addition of ingredients with different textures will add variety. A side salad is a good example of providing a contrast to a pasta dish in both terms of texture and colour.

Thickening

Flours, starchy vegetables and bread can all be used to thicken soups, stews and sauces.

4.5 Food preparation

The aim of food preparation is to produce food that is:

- attractive and nutritious to eat
- safe to eat

The food industry is also concerned with satisfying consumer demand by:

- providing an increased and varied range of products
- maintaining a supply of consistent quality products

Primary and secondary processing

Primary processing is the conversion of the raw produce into edible foodstuffs, e.g. washing and trimming of fruit and vegetables, or its conversion into materials suitable for making edible foodstuffs, e.g. milling wheat into flour.

Secondary processing is the conversion of the products of primary processing into edible foodstuffs, e.g. flour into bread, cane into sugar, pre-prepared foods.

Food hygiene

For food to be safe to eat it is important that it is prepared, cooked and stored hygienically. Good practice depends on a number of factors, all of which must be observed to the highest standards possible.

Raw materials

Do not use materials that are in any way unfit for consumption. When buying food, do so from establishments that are well run and that provide fresh products that have been stored properly. Carefully check any date marks that should be displayed.

Water quality

As water is used throughout the preparation and cooking process, it is essential that an adequate, uncontaminated water supply is available.

Personal hygiene of food handlers

The personal cleanliness of all food handlers must be maintained to the highest standards. This includes:

- wearing of clean overalls, tying back hair and using head coverings
- washing hands in hot, soapy water before and during handling food – especially between handling cooked and uncooked foods or using the toilet
- not smoking when preparing food
- not working when ill and protecting cuts and grazes adequately

Preventing food contamination

Storing food properly and avoide cross-contamination of cooked foods with raw foods, either by contact or the utensils used.

Kitchen hygiene

Maintain clean equipment and surfaces at all times by regular washing with hot, soapy water. The use of anti-bacterial sprays is recommended. Kitchen cloths should be changed regularly and bleached when washed. Rubbish bins should be cleared regularly to avoid attracting pests.

Food business premises should

- be clean and in good repair
- have an adequate water supply
- have adequate sanitary facilities
- have adequate lighting and ventilation
- have suitable pest control arrangements
- be designed to take account of good hygiene practices

Cooking food

Food is cooked for the following reasons:

- to make it easier to eat
- to improve the resulting flavour of the food by combination and the addition of spices and herbs, etc.
- to make it safer to eat as heating to a high enough temperature will kill harmful bacteria
- to enable it to be kept longer

The heat necessary for cooking is passed to the food in three ways:

- conduction – by placing the food in or on a substance that is hot, e.g. in a saucepan of boiling water or in a frying pan
- convection – by placing the food in an atmosphere that is heated, e.g in an oven
- radiation – by placing the food in the direct rays of the heat source, e.g. under a grill

A **microwave oven** works by food molecules, especially water and fat, absorbing microwave energy and vibrating. This generates heat and the food cooks by conduction. It is a method that is especially useful for reheating, defrosting and cooking high water or fat content foods quickly. Because the oven does not cook the food evenly, cold spots can occur. The food should be rotated regularly and left to stand to allow conduction to take place.

Food preservation

Food spoils because of the action of micro-organisms which require warmth, moisture and time to multiply. They can be put into three groups:

- yeasts – use the sugar in foods to reproduce and give off carbon dioxide (a process known as fermentation). Although this is useful in such processes as bread making and wine making, it can spoil other foods.

- bacteria – although some bacteria are useful to food production, e.g in yoghurt and cheese, others are positively harmful and can cause food poisoning as well as spoilage.

- moulds – grow when the spores of fungi fall on the surface of foods. Some, as in blue cheese are encouraged, but others will produce harmful toxins.

Enzymes, although not micro-organisms, change food such as fruit by making it go brown and by destroying the vitamin content.

To preserve food, the following methods can be used:

- chemicals – vinegar, sugar, salt and smoke all contain chemicals that can destroy micro-organisms by removing the water from the food (dehydration).

- chilling – if cooked food is quickly chilled to just above 0°C and kept at a temperature below 8°C, the growth of the majority of bacteria is halted. It is important therefore that strict hygiene conditions are observed during the preparation, handling and transportation of chilled foods and that the temperature is maintained below this critical level.

  It is essential that refrigerator compartments are kept at below 5°C.

- drying – once again, by removing water from the food the microorganisms cannot grow. They must not be allowed to get damp during storage, but can readily be rehydrated when required.

  Liquids, such as milk and soups, are dried using a process called **spray drying**. The liquid is sprayed as a fine mist into a hot air chamber where it turns to a powder.

  Solid foods, such as vegetables and pulses, are dried on **hot air beds** (much the same as traditionally being left in the sun to dry as is still done with many fruits in hot, dry countries).

  Frozen foods can be dried using **accelerated freeze drying**, which drives off the ice as water vapour in a vacuum at low pressure. This process does not damage the food or spoil its flavour or colour - it is suitable for heat sensitive foods and can be used for instant coffee granules.

- irradiation – will kill all micro-organisms. However, this is still a controversial method of preservation and, though allowed by law in the UK, it is not widely used. Irradiated food must be clearly labelled as such by law.

- freezing – once water is frozen, micro-organisms and enzymes become inactive. In order for food to keep its shape and appearance, especially after defrosting, it is important that the freezing process reduces the temperature from 0°C to – 4°C in less than 30 minutes so that only small ice crystals develop.

Blanching – immersion in boiling water – will also improve the quality of frozen vegetables by stopping the enzymes and reducing vitamin loss.

Industrial methods of freezing include **plate freezing** for flat foods, **blast freezing** for bulkier goods such as vegetables where very cold air is blasted around them and **cryogenic or immersion freezing** which uses liquid nitrogen. The latter is expensive but, as it freezes almost immediately, it is very effective for delicate fruits.

It is essential that domestic freezers are kept below –18°C, whereas commercial freezers operate at –29°C. Once frozen food has defrosted it should never be refrozen.

- heating – as heat (preferably above 72°C) kills micro-organisms and enzymes, it is a useful means of preserving food that is to be bottled or canned. The canning process involves placing the food in the can and, in the case of meat and vegetable, then sealing it before it is heated to 115°C.

- modified atmosphere packing (MAP) – seals the food in an atmosphere of carbon dioxide and nitrogen gas which almost completely replaces the oxygen and therefore slows down the growth of micro-organisms.

- Vacuum packing – removes all the oxygen from the packaging which prevents the growth of micro-organisms. As with MAP, once the packet has had its seal broken, it must be treated as fresh food.

E **xaminer's tip**

You are advised to remember the significance of these critical temperatures:

–18°C maximum freezer temperature
5°C maximum refrigerator temperature
8°C maximum chilled food storage temperature
5°C – 63°C danger zone for the multiplication of bacteria
72°C minimum maintained temperature that food should be heated to throughout

4.6 Food labelling

The labels that are put on food packages generally provide the information required by the Food Safety Act and the Food Labelling Regulations 1995. They also include other information that the manufacturer feels will promote its product and are therefore useful for the following reasons:

- product recognition
- dietary information
- storage and preparation
- comparison with other similar products

Product name

The name must either describe the product, be a name generally used in the region where it is sold or be legally established. A subtitle must be added to a name if it fails to adequately describe the food and must also indicate whether the food has undergone any process such as 'smoking'.

If a picture is included on the packet, it must not indicate anything that would mislead the consumer such as depicting real fruit in a dish that only contains fruit flavouring.

Name and address

The country of origin and the full name and address of the manufacturer or packer.

List of ingredients

The ingredients used in the manufacture of the food are listed in **descending** order of weight. Any additives used are also included using their specific names and/or the approved E numbers. The type of additive should also be indicated, e.g. preservative, before the name.

Some manufacturers also indicate the percentage of the total weight of some ingredients. This method of labelling is known as '**quantitive ingredient declaration**', or QUID.

The **average** weight or volume of the product that the package should contain must also be included.

User and storage instructions

Cooking and reheating instructions are especially useful on products such as ready meals, as are instructions on how to store the product before and after opening the packet.

Shelf life

This refers to how long the product can be kept before the packet is opened. After this, the storage instructions will have to be followed to avoid spoilage. The date codes indicating 'shelf life' come in a number of forms:

- Use by – used for highly perishable foods which are usually only chilled and thus more liable to become a health risk. Once the date shown has passed, the food is likely to deteriorate rapidly.

- Best before – for longer lasting items having less potential for microbioligical spoiling, a 'best before' date is given in the form of the day and the month for items with a shelf life of less than three months, and with the year included for longer lasting items.

- Best before end – with items that can last over eighteen months, the month and year, or even just the year, need only to be given.

Other information that is often given, but not required by the regulations, is 'display until'. This date is often set a few days before any other form of date coding in order that the customer has some leeway after purchasing. Retailers will often mark down the price of items that have passed their 'display until' date in order to promote their sale. Fresh fruit and vegetables will often have this form of coding as they are not legally required to have the other forms.

Frozen foods benefit from having the 'star marking' system which indicates how long the product may be stored in a freezer cabinet or compartment.

Star marking	Consume within
*	1 week of purchase
**	1 month of purchase
***	3 months of purchase

Nutritional information

Unless the food company is making a specific claim about the nutritional value of a product, it is not required to include nutritional information on the label, although it is now common practice to do so as the consumer has become more health conscious. This information is usually given in terms of a fixed weight or volume so that direct comparisons can be made, e.g. per 100 grams, or in terms of a fixed portion of the product.

Examiner's tip

You are advised to compare a range of packaged foods by disassembling them from the information contained on the labels. Observations should be made on how the types and proportion of the ingredients and the manufacturing processes have contributed to the product's overall characteristics and ability to meet a specific need.

Other information

Symbols are sometimes included to readily indicate other features of the product. These are illustrated in Fig. 4.3.

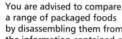

- Suitable for freezing

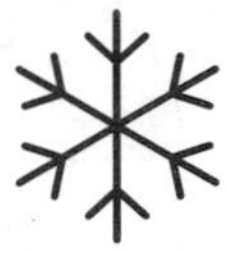

- Suitable for heating in a microwave

- Suitable for vegetarians

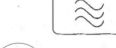

Fig. 4.3 Symbols used in labelling

4.7 Packaging

Examiner's tip

As packaging constitutes about 25% of household waste, you should concentrate on ways of reducing packaging by limiting its use to what is essential, re-using containers and recycling the rest.

The packaging that food comes in has a number of practical advantages:

- ease of transportation and handling at point of sale
- ease of storage and display
- protects from damage and contamination
- increased shelf life
- convenient for labelling and other information

However, the food companies invest a lot of time and money in the packaging they use because of the product recognition and brand loyalty that their advertising and marketing is trying to achieve.

Materials for packaging

Glass

- although easily broken and comparatively heavy, has the advantages of being re-usable and readily recycled
- forms the greatest proportion of waste packaging
- is extremely good for liquids and can be used in a microwave
- can be printed on, but a label is usually added.

Metal
- aluminium and steel form the next most common element in packaging, being both rigid and strong and a good barrier to liquid and gas
- is readily recyclable and easily printed on although labels are still commonly used
- is high in energy costs to produce and needs coating to prevent reaction with contents
- cannot be used in a microwave

Plastic
- available in a rigid form as well as a film
- not as strong as glass or metal but much lighter
- can be produced in a flexible form and moulded into intricate shapes
- available in a wide range of colours and capable of being printed on
- good moisture barrier and inert to most foods
- not readily recycled, but progress is being made all the time to make it economically viable to do so

Paper and board
- light and reasonably strong, it often forms the outer packaging to improve features of other forms of packing
- readily printed and recycled
- poor protection against moisture
- chemicals used in its production could contaminate some foods if direct contact is made

Tamper-proof packing

On page 87 the system of preservation by MAP and vacuum packing was discussed, where either the gas inside the packet is changed or removed altogether. It is obviously important that this type of packet remains sealed until needed. This is also true of other packaged items such as baby foods, which must remain airtight for health reasons.

There have also been instances of malicious tampering with food products, and therefore food companies have developed a number of ways of indicating that the seal has been broken in some way – shrink wraps, plastic break collars and paper sealing strips.

Other information

As already noted, the packaging is the main vehicle for food labelling and promoting the product/brand image. Companies often use packaging for other marketing strategies such as recipes, money-off coupons and free gifts of all kinds. Examples of other factual information are presented in Fig. 4.4.

Description	Symbol
Environmental symbols, indicating the use of recycled materials or that the materials used can be recycled.	
Litterman symbol, used to encourage the proper disposal of the packing.	
Bar code, used to aid computerised stock handling and checkout facilities. Each product has its own identifying bar code.	5 000183 522233

Fig. 4.4 Information displayed on packaging

4.8 Product development

The aim of the food industry is to satisfy demands based on consumer needs. Consumer needs vary from those of basic nutrition to those of pure enjoyment. Financial considerations also play a large part in consumer demand.

The successful company will achieve this by:

- maintaining the consistent quality of existing products that are healthy and pleasant to eat
- providing an increased and varied range of products
- developing new methods and systems which increase efficiency and reduce waste
- reacting quickly to changes in consumer buying habits and lifestyles
- promoting brand names and brand loyalty

Product ideas

New ideas for products will be generated for a number of reasons:

- reduced market share of existing products
- new products from competitors
- changes in technology
- changes due to health related issues
- gap in product range
- special occasions or minority needs

Initial feasibility studies are carried out at this stage to consider:

- if there is a genuine market for such a product
- if the potential selling price covers the costs of development, launching and production and thus generates a profit
- if the product can be produced effectively

Recipe formulation

Once the product specification has been generated and the initial screening suggests that it is potentially successful, a recipe is formulated in order that tests may be carried out. At this stage, the recipe is developed on a domestic scale – a one-off or small batch – taking account of the criteria given, such as main ingredient, type of dish, method of cooking and storage, size of portion. A deep knowledge of the nutritional and working properties of food must be applied along with an inventive approach to combinations and textures.

Each of the test samples must come with a complete reference which will include:

- exact list of ingredients
- processing methods
- serving details

Sensory testing

The development team will include a group of tasters who have experience of testing new products in terms of taste and flavour, aroma, consistency and texture (mouth feel) and appearance. These qualities are termed **organoleptic**.

Some of the samples will be rejected and others will have suggestions made for modifications. This continues until there is an agreed group of samples to take forward for further market research.

Evaluation tests: a panel of people are simply asked to indicate, on a predetermined scale, how much they like or dislike a product. The tasting will often take place under coloured lights so that the colour of the food will not affect the response to other sensory descriptors.

This will only give an idea as to the potential success of a product. More sophisticated sensory tests need to be carried out to refine the product.

Descriptive tests

- the panel is asked to place a number of samples in order with reference to a certain characteristic. This is known as a **ranking** test. Symbols are often used to designate each sample to avoid any subconscious effect that numbering or lettering may have on the taster.
- the panel is asked to score the sample on a numerical scale with reference to a number of characteristics. This is known as a **rating** test.

The results of a rating test can be plotted on a **star profile**, with each arm of the star representing a sensory descriptor. The star profiles can then be compared easily and the basis for further adjustments formulated.

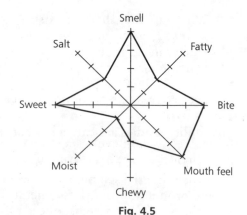

Fig. 4.5

Discrimination tests

- **paired comparison tests** are used to test two samples to see if the taster can tell the difference between them with respect to a specific characteristic

- **triangle tests** are used to test small differences in samples, often in an attempt to replicate another product. The taster is asked to find the 'odd one out', having been told that two out of the three samples are identical

- **taste threshold tests** are used to determine how little of a substance needs to be added to achieve the desired result, e.g. salt

Technical development

Once the testing has generated a preferred recipe, the formulation is scaled up to allow a trial production run. This will check that the recipe can be made with the production facilities available. Should any alterations need to be made to any of the working properties, a further test will be carried out to determine whether there have been any changes to the flavour. Further organoleptic tests will be carried out to verify the results of the batch production samples.

During the factory technical development trials, the process is checked at all the **critical control points** to prove the system is working to specification and to carry out **hazard identification** to control risks (**risk assessment**) – especially with respect to contamination.

Critical control points

The process is monitored regularly at these points and **feedback** given to enable corrective action to be taken. The efficiency of this **closed loop** system can be critical to the profitability of a product – especially if there is a potentially high risk process involved. See Unit 1.4 for further information on systems and control.

Control points will often include:

- raw materials arrival – should be checked for condition and arrangements made for suitable storage and preparation when potential contamination hazards can be identified

- recipe formulation – checks are made to verify that the correct ingredients are being used and that the quantities are within the agreed tolerances

- cooking – temperature and time are constantly monitored

- cooling – the time taken to cool prior to packing must be constantly monitored

- handling and packing – hygiene regimes are important at this stage

This system of analysing the risks involved at the various stages of the production process and then monitoring closely these areas during production is a safety system known as **hazard analysis and critical control points** (**HACCP**).

Production

While the technical development has been in progress, the packaging has been designed in line with the company image and a marketing strategy developed so that production can start and the product can be launched with maximum market penetration.

4.9 Computers in food technology

Data handling

Computer spreadsheets are used to analyse and present the information from sensory testing, questionnaires used in market research, costings, etc.

Nutrition analysis

Food products can readily have their nutritional value calculated by the use of programmes containing all the relevant data with respect to the ingredients and processes used in the production.

Computer control in manufacture

Most batch and mass production systems will use computers to monitor and control much of the production process. This will range from stock control and ordering, through monitoring the critical control points and automatically making the adjustments required, to packaging and despatch of the finished product.

Chapter 5
Graphic products

5.1 Equipment

You will be expected to be able to use the following:

- drawing board – preferably A3 size, and T square
- 60°/30° and 45° set squares
- compasses and dividers
- 300mm rule and protractor
- eraser and eraser shield
- pencils
  - 2B }
  - HB } for shading / toning
  - 3H for lining in
  - 6H for construction
- pencil sharpener
- coloured pencils
- fine liners – 0.1, 0.3, 0.5 and 0.7
- templates

If available and relevant, the following equipment could be used:

- air brush
- computer aided drawing (CAD)
- marker pens
- dry transfers
- colour wash
- photocopier
- lightbox

Examiner's tip

This is the minimum requirement – you may wish to use a greater range to enhance your work. However, care must be taken when using softer pencils, and it is advisable to use a fixative.

Examiner's tip

The quality of the pencils you use will directly affect the quality of your work. It is worth the extra to obtain a good set, which will also last you a long time if looked after.

5.2 Types of illustration

There are four basic types of illustration that you can use in a project or in the examination. They differ in terms of the time taken and their accuracy.

Freehand sketch

This method relies purely on you using the pencil and/or pen on its own to produce the illustration. It is the quickest method, often used for initial ideas or quick explanations.

Sketch

This is the same as freehand sketch, but you 'crate out' the basic shape first using a rule or other piece of equipment to help you, before putting in the required detail freehand. This will obviously take more time but may often achieve a more satisfactory end result for many pupils. However, *do not* use this method in an examination if you have specifically been asked for a 'freehand sketch'.

Drawing

Once you start to develop ideas more fully, it is often desirable to produce a more accurate looking illustration. Drawings will use instruments much more and will endeavour to maintain proportion. They will not require complete accuracy in terms of dimensions, angles, etc.

Note: All of the above three methods may be rendered as required to enhance the detail – see Unit 5.3.

Construction

Usually used for finished or working drawings. These will obey conventions and will be dimensionally accurate. They are unlikely to be rendered, but will sometimes be dimensioned. Constructed drawings will usually take the longest time to produce.

5.3 Rendering

Rendering is the application of line, pencil, colour, marker, ink, etc. to give an impression of depth, light and shade, texture or material in order to make the representation more realistic.

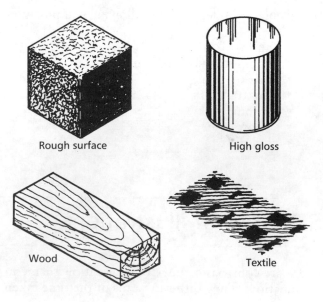

Rough surface   High gloss

Wood   Textile

Fig. 5.1 Applied rendering to achieve different material and finish effects

5.4 Pictorial representation

The aim of much graphic work is to give a three–dimensional representation using a two–dimensional medium. This unit will highlight the main methods of achieving this. It is up to you to use the most appropriate form to achieve the desired effect.

Oblique

This is the simplest form of drawing in *three dimensions*, and is often the way younger and less experienced pupils will try to draw naturally. You start by drawing a true 'front view' of the object. All horizontal lines are then taken back at 45° and scaled down to half size. Note that the centre for a radius is also moved along the 45° axis.

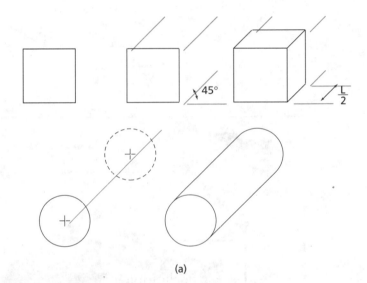

(a)

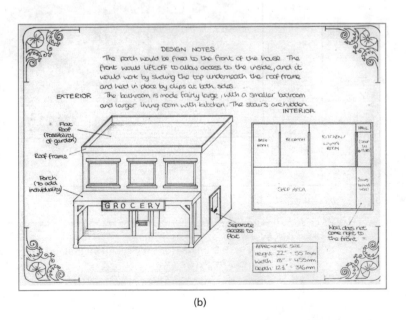

(b)

Fig. 5.2   (a) Stages in oblique drawing   (b) Example of oblique used in project work

Isometric

This method does not rely on the object being orientated in such a way that one true face can be drawn and therefore produces a more natural effect. All vertical lines remain vertical, but lines representing horizontal planes are drawn at an angle of 30° to the horizontal. It should be noted that as the length of lines on the vertical and 30° axes remain true scale, the end result can turn out larger than expected!

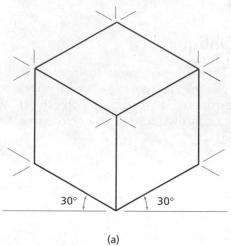

(a)

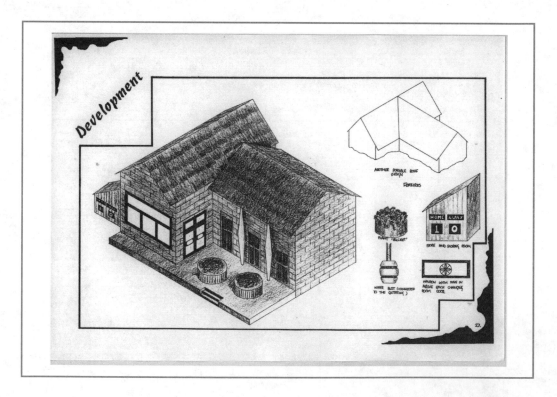

(b)

Fig. 5.3 (a) An isometric cube   (b) Example of isometric used in project work

Circles in isometric become ellipses, which have a major and a minor axis. Use the line of the major axis, and the knowledge that a circle touches the mid points of the sides of the square that encloses it to locate points through which you can draw the ellipse.

If you have an ellipse template, the major axis should also be used to align the marks on the template, once you have selected the appropriate size ellipse to fit your requirements.

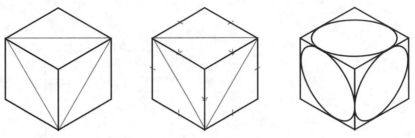

Fig. 5.4 Stages in drawing isometric circles

Isometric circles – construction

Two methods for constructing circles in isometric are shown in Fig. 5.5.

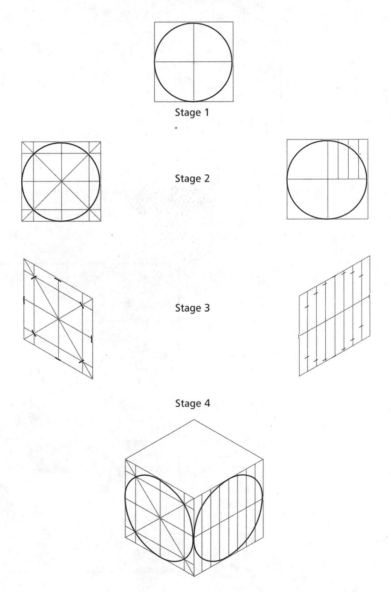

Fig. 5.5 Constructing circles in isometric

Planometric

When designing such things as room layouts, it is useful to give a three-dimensional impression of the effect. The plan view is drawn to scale, and then turned through either 30° or 45°. The vertical lines are then projected and the objects completed. It is more effective to leave out all, or part of, the two near walls to give a more 'open view'.

Note, that in the case of a 45° planometric, the vertical scale is 3/4.

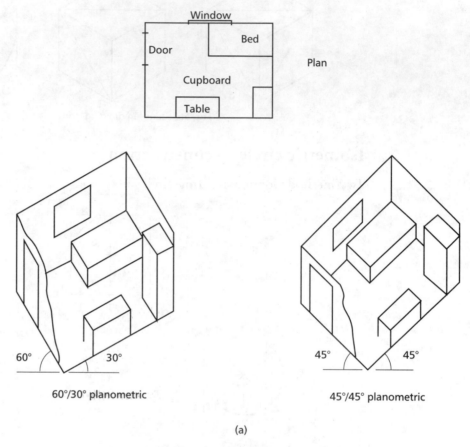

60°/30° planometric   45°/45° planometric

(a)

(b)

Fig. 5.6 (a) Planometric (b) Example of 45° planometric in project work

One-point perspective

You will have noticed that none of the preceding methods gives truly realistic results. This is because they do not take account of perspective. This method uses the principle that all horizontal lines that are moving away from the viewer meet at a single point on the horizon (vanishing point – VP) at eye level.

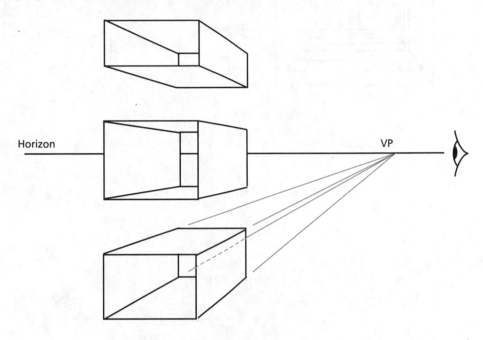

Fig. 5.7 One-point perspective

Two-point perspective

One-point perspective still gives a rather 'flat' effect – this can be improved upon by the use of two-point perspective. This assumes that horizontal lines moving away from the viewer to the right and left meet at two separate VPs, still on the horizon at eye level.

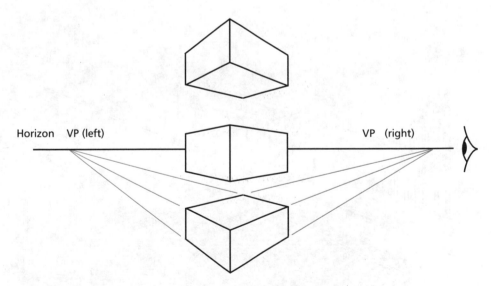

Fig. 5.8. Two-point perspective

Estimated depth in perspective

Due to foreshortening, you would expect objects to appear smaller, the further away from the viewer they are. If your perspective scene contains elements that are regularly spaced then the following methods will allow you to produce this effect more accurately.

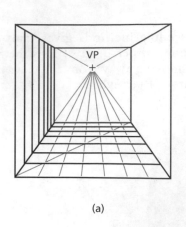

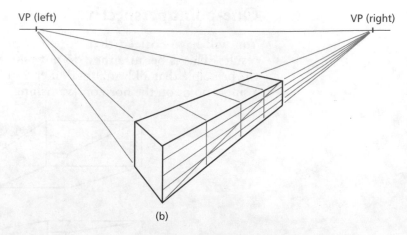

(a)

(b)

Fig. 5.9 (a) One-point perspective (b) Two-point perspective

Fig. 5.10 One-point perspective

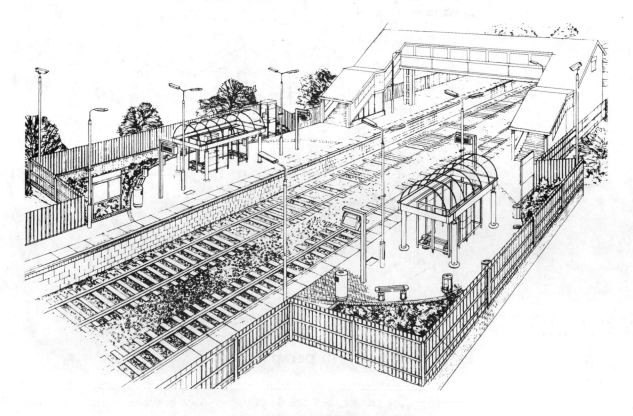

Fig. 5.11 Two-point perspective

Perspective shadow

Another way of enhancing your perspective drawing is to add shadow. This assumes that if you follow your shadow back towards the horizon it will end directly underneath the light source, i.e. the sun.

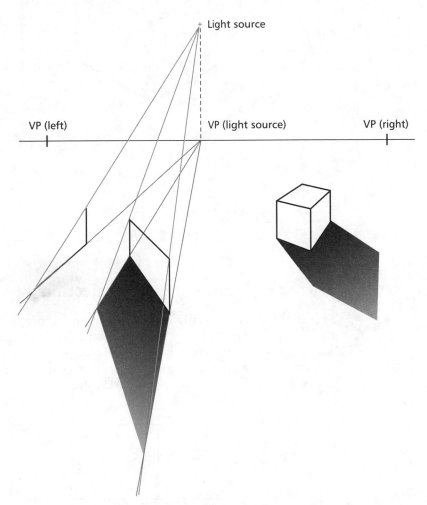

Fig. 5.12 Two-point perspective shadow

Some points to remember:

- place the light source as high as possible giving shorter shadows
- keep the light source to one side of the object
- treat the object as a series of flag poles, connected at the top by a taut string!

Thick and thin

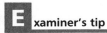
xaminer's tip

This is an excellent method for the application of fine liners, where you could use 0.3 and 0.7 liners for the thin and thick lines respectively. Remember, you must hold them vertically or you will not achieve a true line thickness and will get undue wear which will shorten the useful life.

When time and/or printing costs are critical factors in the production of an illustration, e.g for a simple throw-away assembly/instruction sheet, and other methods of rendering are considered inappropriate, then the simplest way of enhancement is the use of thick and thin lines.

The rule to be applied is:

- if you can see **both** surfaces that form the line, it is drawn **thin**
- if you can only see **one** surface that forms the line, it is drawn **thick**

A thick line is drawn approximately **twice** the thickness of a thin line.

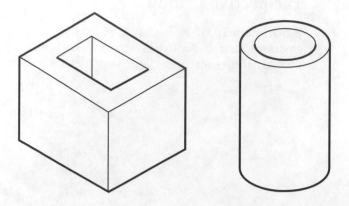

Fig. 5.13 Thick and thin applied to isometric drawings

5.5 Formal drawings

Third angle orthographic projection

This is the internationally recognised form for presenting technical drawings (first angle is now rarely used) which contain all the required information accurately drawn to scale so that others can manufacture the object. They are commonly known as *working drawings*, because they will sometimes also contain details of joints, materials, construction methods, etc.

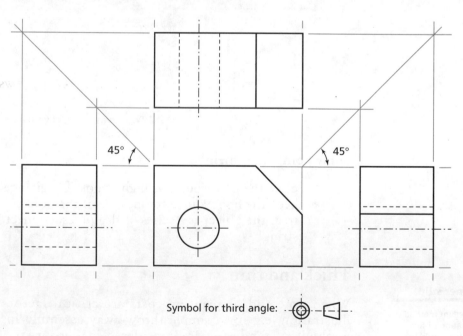

45°   45°

Symbol for third angle:

Fig. 5.14 Construction method for third-angle projection

Although four views are shown here, three are usually sufficient – especially in an examination.

Section views

In some cases, the standard orthographic views – even with hidden detail, or because of it – will not clearly indicate the true shape or construction of an object. A section view will assist this.

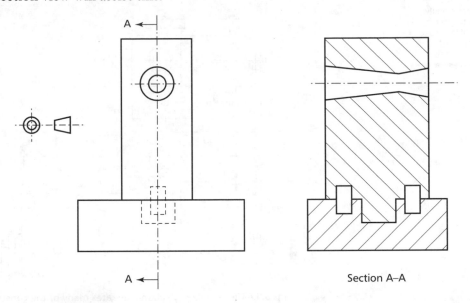

Fig. 5.15 Sectioned view in third-angle orthographic

Some points to remember:

- 'cut' the object down the section line, remove the part behind the arrows and draw the remainder as normal. Cross hatch anything that has been 'cut'
- do not cross hatch thin items such as webs, nuts, bolts, screws, etc.
- use different cross hatching for different pieces of the object
- label the section line and the view, ensuring the arrows conform to third angle
- no hidden detail is to be included in section views

Dimensioning

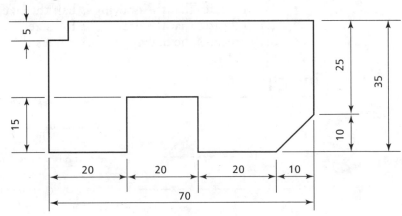

Fig. 5.16 Dimensioning

Some points to remember:

- dimensions are written above the dimension line
- vertical dimensions are read from the right-hand side (turn the drawing through 90°)
- you should use millimetres at all times and note it only once in the title block

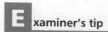

E xaminer's tip

This aspect can adversely affect an orthographic drawing if it is done badly. You are advised to refer to BS7308, a booklet issued by the British Standards Institute.

- arrow heads are long and thin and do not dominate the drawing
- dimension limit lines stop short of the object by 2mm
- the smallest dimensions are put nearest the object
- do not dimension inside the object

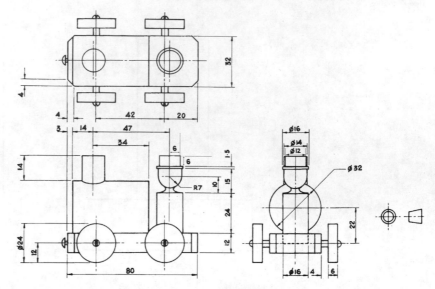

Fig. 5.17 Third-angle projection illustrates many of the construction details

Scale

All orthographic drawings must be drawn to a scale which is noted in the title block.

Note Any dimensions added to a drawing, whatever the scale, will be the true dimensions – it is only the drawing that is scaled.

A scale is a **ratio** and therefore has no units. Convention is that the scale of a drawing is the ratio between the drawing and the object, *not* the other way round.

Therefore a scale of:

- 1:2 indicates that the drawing is half the size of the object
- 1:1 indicates that the drawing is full size
- 3:1 indicates the drawing is three times the size of the object

Line types

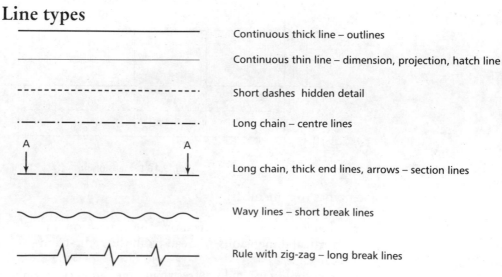

Fig. 5.18 Line types for working drawings

Exploded views

These views are extremely useful for assembly and instruction leaflets as they indicate the various parts of an object in their *relative positions* without obscuring each other.

The most common form of drawing used is isometric, the components being moved apart strictly along the 90° and 30° axes. Dotted guidelines are used to clarify the relative locations of some components if doubt could exist.

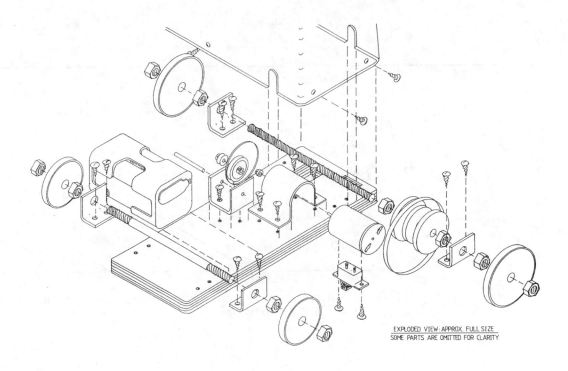

EXPLODED VIEW: APPROX. FULL SIZE
SOME PARTS ARE OMITTED FOR CLARITY

(a)

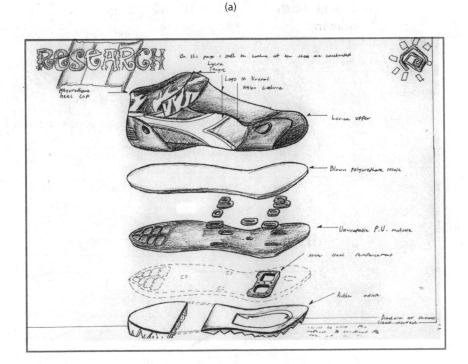

(b)

Fig. 5.19 (a) Exploded view of battery-powered motor (b) Example of exploded drawing

5.6 Geometrical constructions

Construct a perpendicular

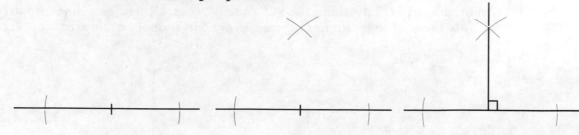

Fig. 5.20

Bisect an angle

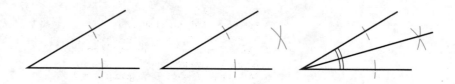

Fig. 5.21

Construct 30°, 45° and 60° angles

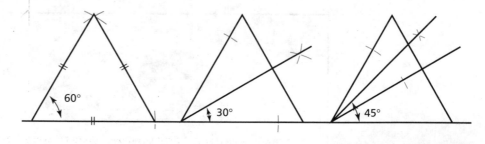

Fig. 5.22

Sub-divide a line

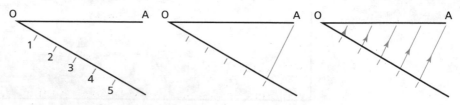

Fig. 5.23 Subdividing line OA into five

Construct regular polygons

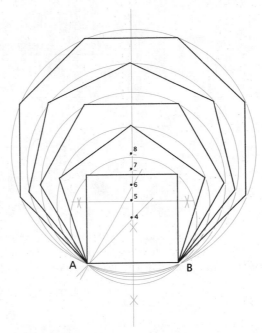

1. Given side AB
2. Perpendicularly bisect side AB
3. From A, construct 45° line giving point 4
4. From A, construct 60° line giving point 6
5. Bisect 4–6, giving point 5
6. Mark off distance 5–6, to give points 7,8 . . . etc.
7. Using 4–A as raduis, draw circle centred at 4.
   (This step is repeated for whichever polygon is required)
8. Using radius, mark off around circumference
9. Complete polygon.

Fig. 5.24

Plotting loci

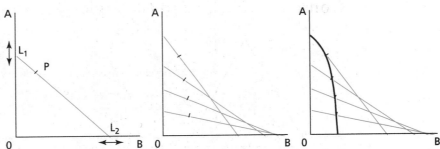

Example: One end of a fixed link moves along OA while the other end moves along OB. Plot the locus of the point P.

Method:
1. Plot the link in a number of positions between the limits of its movement
2. Plot the position of the point in each case
3. Draw in locus of the point P.

Fig. 5.25

Developments

Many containers and packages are formed from a single sheet of material by cutting, scoring, folding, interlocking and gluing of tabs. The flat forms of such containers are called the developments (sometimes also known as nets).

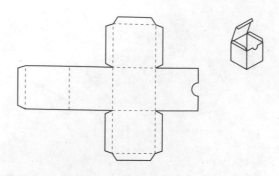

Fig. 5.26

The design of such developments is a critical process in the packaging industry, as is the way the developments are arranged on the sheet material to avoid waste. When shapes naturally fit together in a regular pattern, it is known as **tessellation**.

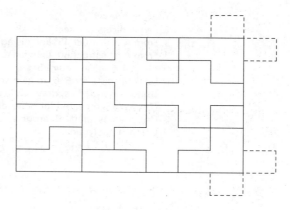

Fig. 5.27 Developments arranged to reduce waste

5.7 Modelling

Modelling is an extremely useful form of communicating ideas, and a model will most likely be the way in which you cover the material requirements of the examination.

Models can be used in a number of ways:

- to try out an early idea in the form of a mock-up
- to test whether something works practically in the form of a working model
- to give an impression of the finished object in the form of a prototype

It must also be remembered that more sophisticated computer programs can 'model' ideas by allowing you to view the drawings from any desired viewpoint.

xaminer's tip

One of the most important things to remember when modelling is **scale**. This may well, in some cases, include the weight of the model.

Modelling tests the inventiveness of the modeller, as the main aim is to give an impression of the object being modelled – not to manufacture it. Therefore, the whole range of materials is available to the modeller, as long as the purpose is achieved.

Some of the more useful modelling materials are listed below.

Construction kits

These are especially useful for developing mechanistic ideas and are used effectively as mock-ups.

Card

The most readily available material and extremely useful as it is available in many grades, thicknesses, colours and finishes. It is easily cut and will accept many different adhesives and applied finishes. It is especially useful for architectural models and, obviously, packaging.

Foamboard

A specialist modelling board, but expensive.

Medium density fibreboard (MDF)

A manufactured board that is much better for modelling than natural timber as it has no grain, is easy to cut and shape, and can be readily joined with the use of wood adhesives such as PVA.

It will also produce an excellent finish with the use of abrasives, and readily accepts applied finishes like cellulose paint sprays which give an extremely realistic effect.

Note As with all manufactured particle boards, cutting and abrading causes a lot of dust. Good extraction and the use of a mask is essential.

Jelutong

Although a natural hardwood, its working qualities are superior to that of MDF and the finish achievable is even better. However, it is expensive and even the off-cuts should be retained for possible future use.

Plastics

Acrylic is often used as a modelling material, but not always with great success as it is reasonably difficult to cut, form and join. It also does not readily accept applied finishes.

Expanded polystyrene is readily available as a waste product from packaging, but is rather coarse and crumbly when worked and is therefore only really suitable for the early development of ideas.

Styrofoam is a fine-celled version of expanded polystyrene which can be cut and formed readily, and finished using fine abrasive papers. It is joined using PVA and can be painted using a water-based emulsion paint.

Note Although polystyrene cuts easily using a hot-wire cutter, the fumes are toxic. Such a cutter should only be used where there are adequate air-extraction facilities and never if the wire is red hot.

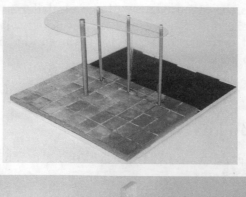

Fig. 5.28 Modelling samples

5.8 Graphs and charts

Often generated from the results of surveys and questionnaires, or by the need to display information in an easily accessible form, graphs, charts and tables allow you to show your graphic communication skills to the full. It is an opportunity to be creative in the selection of the most appropriate form of communication.

5.9 Flow charts

Flow charts are extremely useful when planning any process and can help determine the 'critical path' – the sequence of events that will control the outcome of the process. A flow chart is not only a sequential list of operations, but it also contains feedback loops and control operations.

The symbols in Fig. 5.29 are used when preparing flow charts.

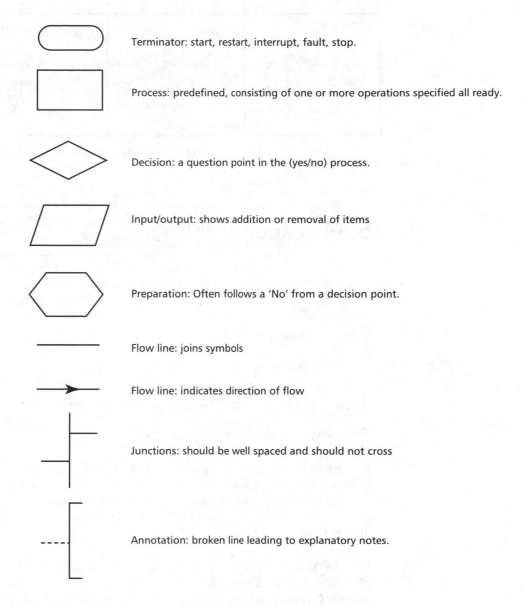

Fig. 5.29 Flow chart symbols

5.10 Sequence diagrams

Sequence diagrams are largely graphic representations of processes designed to exemplify, and in many instances even take the place of, verbal or written instructions.

Points to remember:

- decide on the space available for the whole illustration
- clearly define the minimum number of stages needed to illustrate the process given the space available
- reduce each stage to its basic components
- produce the graphics that clearly illustrate each stage, avoiding unnecessary embellishment
- add notation if required (or allowed!)

Fig. 5.30 Sequence diagram for making a cup of tea

5.11 Paper and board

The description of any paper or board should indicate:

- type
- colour and finish
- size
- grammage

Types of paper and board and their uses

The most commonly used raw materials are :

Mechanical wood pulp: made by mechanically grinding down about 90% of the debarked tree to almost saw-dust sized chips and so uses the wood very efficiently. It contains short fibres and impurities which weaken it and produces paper of poor colour which ages quickly when exposed to light. It is therefore used for the cheaper grades of paper.

Chemical wood pulp: a purer form of wood pulp which is ground less finely but chemically treated to remove the unwanted impurities. The longer fibres produce a stronger, cleaner paper. However, it only uses about 50% of the debarked tree.

Recycled paper and board: an important source of raw material, especially as the pressure increases on the need to preserve the natural timber resource and the economics of recycling become more attractive. However, each time paper is recycled, the fibres lose strength and become suitable only for lower-quality products.

Rags: cotton, linen, hemp, manila and jute have all been used for producing 'rag papers', but the best quality comes from cotton and linen. The long fibres make the paper strong and durable, and for some uses it is are considered the best quality of paper to use. However, this paper is expensive to produce.

The more commonly used papers are:

Newsprint: made from mechanical wood pulp and the cheapest grade of printing paper – supplied in reels or sheets. It is mainly used for newspaper type products as it will readily accept the inks used in their production.

Mechanical printing: a superior newsprint, containing more chemical wood pulp. It is used for cheap publications and writing paper.

Mechanical SC printing: used for mass circulation magazines and cheaper books.

Woodfree printings: contain no mechanical wood pulp and are used for all kinds of general printing.

Cartridge: used for printing as well as drawing, being produced in a range of surface finishes.

Offset printings: used for litho printing.

Coated papers: are given different surface treatments and finishes and are produced in various forms for specialised uses.

Banks and bonds: produced with a matt surface for typewriting and handwriting.

Duplicators: have a soft, matt finish and are slightly absorbent making them suitable for duplicating processes, where a good impression is required.

Cover papers: a wide range of strongly coloured papers that are usually thick with good folding and wearing qualities and are therefore used as covers for booklets and brochures. When laminated, they produce a thicker paper known as cover board.

A considerable number of the above papers are also available as board weights which generally start at 200 g/m^2. The most commonly used boards are:

Pulp board: produced in various qualities and finishes.

Index board: resembles pulp board – comes in a range of tints and has a high machine finish suitable for printing and writing. Used for office records and card index systems.

Paste board: more rigid than pulp board with a core lined on both surfaces and a tinted lining paper of higher quality. Two or more sheets may be combined to give greater thickness as duplex or triplex boards.

Finishes

Apart from the fibres of a paper, over 30% of the weight of a paper is made up of additives which determine its quality, printability and general characteristics. The main additives are:

Fillers: minerals used to fill the gaps between the fibres to produce a smoother surface.

Sizing: synthetic or resinous materials used to bind fibres and fillers together, retarding water penetration and the spread of inks.

Colouring: dyestuffs and whitening agents used to produce the desired colour.

The manufacturing processes and the ingredients used for the different types will determine the finish of the paper. Papers can be finished smooth, glazed, coarse, embossed, watermarked, coated, etc. The application of a transparent plastic film, known as lamination, will also enhance the appearance and durability.

Standard sizes

Although paper and board is still supplied in many different sizes, both trimmed and untrimmed, most papers are now supplied based on the International Standards Organisation 'A', 'B' and 'C' ranges – the most commonly used being the ISO A-sized items.

The B range items fill the gaps in the A range and are intended primarily for poster work. The C range items are for finished envelopes and folders which will contain the A-sized items.

The basis for the A range is a rectangle of area of one square metre (1 000 000 mm^2), the sides of which are in the ratio of one to the square root of two (1:1.414) – 841 mm × 1180 mm, and is designated A0 . This ratio has the property of being retained when the longer side is halved or the shorter side is doubled.

This gives the following standard sizes :

A range	B range	C range
2A0 1189 × 1682	2B0 1414 × 2000	
A0 841 × 1189	B0 1000 × 1414	
A1 594 × 841	B1 707 × 1000	
A2 420 × 594	B2 500 × 707	
A3 297 × 420	B3 353 × 500	
A4 210 × 297	B4 250 × 353	C4 229 × 324
A5 148 × 210	B5 176 × 250	C5 162 × 229
A6 105 × 148	B6 125 × 176	C6 114 × 162
A7 74 × 105	B7 88 × 125	C7 81 × 114
A8 52 × 74	B8 62 × 88	C8 57 × 81

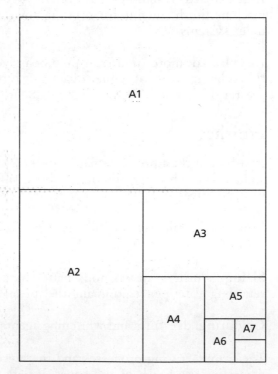

Fig. 5.31 The A range of papers obtained by halving the longer dimension of the basic A0 sheet

Grammage

The standard international sizes are stocked in a range of standard grammages which indicates the weight in grammes of one square metre of the paper or board – g/m^2.

5.12 Lettering

Size of type

The size of any typeface is based on a method of measurement known as the *point system*. One point (1pt) measures 0.351mm. The standard 12pt measurement is called the *pica*.

When a type is described as a certain point size, it refers not to the height of the letter, but to the *body size* of the type, i.e. the distance between one line and the next. However, it is sometimes desirable to increase the space between lines – leading or interlinear spacing. This is achieved by putting a smaller point type on a larger point body size.

Example:

_This is 24pt type,
_using a 24pt body.

_This is an 18pt type,
_using a 24pt body.

The sizes up to 12pt are traditionally known as *composition sizes*, while those from 14pt to 72pt are known as *display sizes*. Larger sizes than 72pt are usually achieved by special headline systems or by enlarging smaller sizes.

Type founts (pronounced 'fonts')

A fount is the term given to an assortment of type characters of the same size and design. This will include the alphabet – upper and lower case, numbers, punctuation marks, reference marks and special signs.

Type characters

The type characters of any fount include the long (J, Q) and short letters (x, a, c), as well as ascending (b, d, f) and descending letters (g, j, p).

As letters are not all of the same width or configuration, to improve the visual appearance some adjustments are made:

Letterspacing: the adjustment of the standard space between characters to remove gaps created by narrower letters.

Kerning: the adjustment of the space still further to allow one part of a letter to extend over the next.

e.g.

Typefaces

A typeface is defined as a set of characters identifiable by design and available in a range of sizes.

Typefaces are grouped into families, and are further changed by adjustments to weight, width, italicising or a combination. A common difference between typefaces is whether the design includes the small strokes at the top and bottom of the main strokes of the letters which are known as *serifs*. Typefaces without serifs are classified as *sanserif*.

5.13 Machine printing

Offset lithography

Offset litho machines can print onto either sheets (sheet fed) or reels (web fed) of paper/board. The basic process consists of a printing plate, containing the image to be printed in relief, being clamped to a cylinder which is rotated. Ink is applied to the plate cylinder which has been wetted with a dampening solution to repel ink from the non-printing areas. The plate cylinder transfers the image to a blanket cylinder rotating in contact with it. The blanket cylinder has a surface coating of synthetic rubber. This cylinder is then pressed against the material to be printed and the final image is transferred.

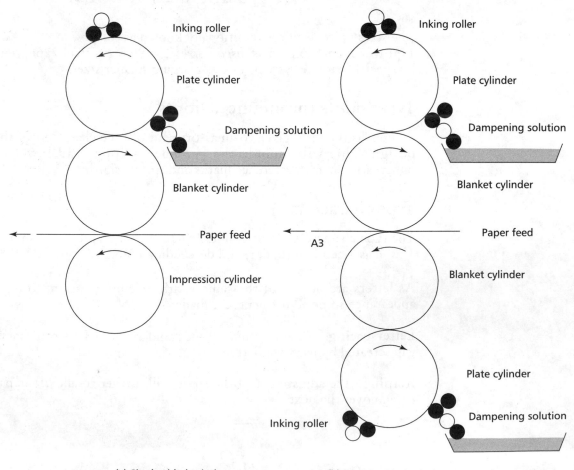

(a) Single-sided printing   (b) Double-sided printing

Fig. 5.32 The basic arrangement for offset presses

Letterpress

Now superseded by other means of rotary printing – especially offset lithography, but is still used for the printing of business cards, leaflets, envelopes. The printing plate is in the form of a relief plate to which the ink is applied by rollers. The paper is laid on a flat casting (platen), dressed with card to avoid damaging the printing plate, and pressed against the plate.

Flexography

This is now the dominant relief printing method. The plate and blanket cylinder are now combined with the image directly engraved onto this cylinder.

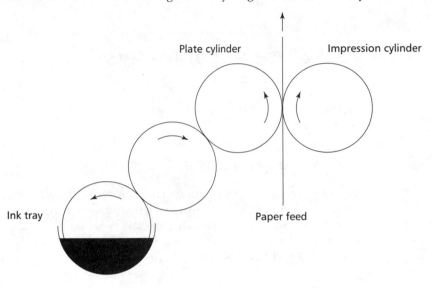

Fig. 5.33 The basic flexographic press

Gravure

In this process the printing cylinder rotates within a trough of ink, the excess being removed by a blade, before having the paper directly fed over it. A very fluid and quick-drying ink is used in this process which is more ideally suited for colour printing with a fast level of output on relatively poor grade, uncoated papers. As non-contaminative solvents can be used, the process is suitable for food wrappings.

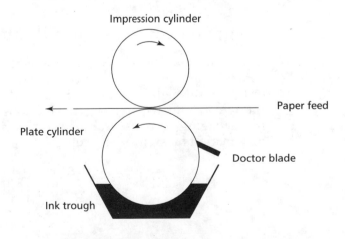

Fig. 5.34 The basic gravure press

Screen

The basic process uses a screen which blocks the passage of the ink from those areas where it is not wanted. The screen is placed onto the paper, and a squeegee forces the ink through the mesh screen onto the paper. This can be done manually or automatically.

This method has a wide range of applications including self-adhesive labels, scratchcards, packaging products, posters, wallpapers and printed circuit boards. It can be applied to many materials such as glass, textiles, metal and rigid plastic. It can also be used for printing on bottles, drums and other containers.

5.14 Use of computers

Much commercial graphic work is now done with the aid of information technology.

Drawing packages

These can be extremely powerful, allowing the designer to create and manipulate images almost at will. **Scanners** will allow existing images to be **imported** into new work and modified. Specialist packages will allow the production of fully detailed working technical drawings, with the more powerful systems able to check accuracy and fit of assembled components.

Computer simulations

Computer simulation is a method of presenting graphic images in a way that allows the viewer to 'experience' the appearance of a product from any viewpoint.

Data handling

Computer spreadsheets are used to analyse all types of data. This data can then be presented as bars charts and graphs in countless ways depending on the package used.

Many of these packages can be imported directly into Desk Top Publishing (DTP) packages for further editing and enhancement.

Computer control in manufacture

Most batch and mass production systems will use computers to monitor and control much of the production process. This will range from stock control and ordering, through monitoring the critical control points and automatically making the adjustments required e.g. the indexing of the different colour runs in printing, to packaging and despatch of the finished product. See Unit 1.4 for further information on systems and control.

Chapter 6

Resistant materials technology

This chapter covers all the essential knowledge for working with resistant materials. However, it is very important that you apply this knowledge to how everyday products work, the materials used in their design and how they are made.

- tin openers
- a computer casing
- a pair of scissors
- a staircase
- a saucepan
- a torch
- a kitchen worktop
- horseshoes
- a school stackable chair
- a kettle

For each of these items, write down (or find out if you don't yet know):

- what materials are used in their construction (be specific! You must name the actual material: wood, metal or plastic is not sufficient)
- why these materials are used, could alternatives be used?
- what mechanical properties are needed in the materials (hardness, strength, heat resistance, etc.)
- how the various parts are made in industry
- how they work (are mechanisms, electronics used)
- why the design (shape, form) is as it is

xaminer's tip

Approach your revision by *applying* your knowledge to products. In the exam you will have to design solutions to problems. You *must* have a sound understanding of how everyday products are made and how they work.

6.1 Tools and equipment

Cutting and shaping tools

Tool	Tool in use	Use on	Notes
Tenon saw	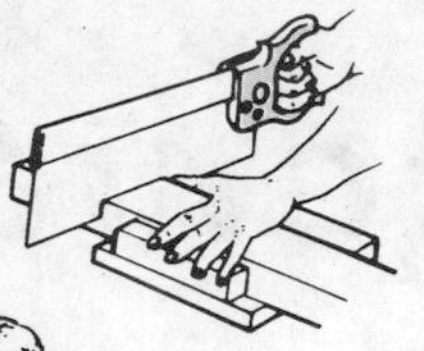	W	Used to cut relatively small pieces of wood and for sawing joints, such as tenons and halvongs
Hand saw		W	Available in different lengths and with different numbers of teeth per cm. Use to saw larger sections of wood
Coping saw	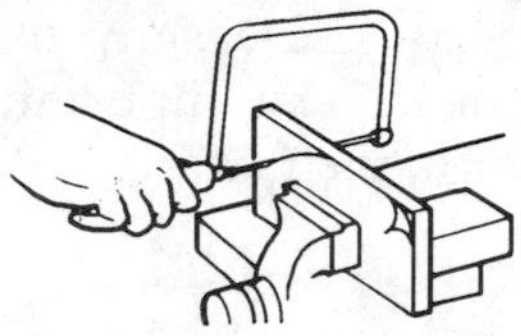	W P	Not ideal for straight cuts but good for curves and removing awkward shapes in wood and some plastics
Firmer chisel	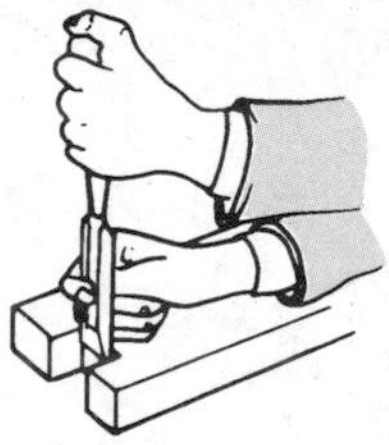	W	Generally used horizontally or vertically (as shown) for removing small amounts of timber accurately
Jack/smoothing plane	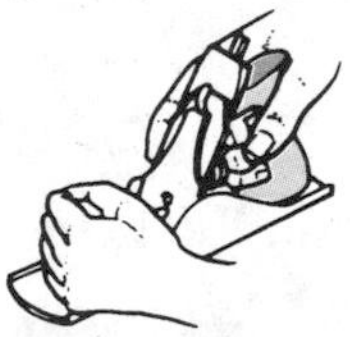	W P	Used to prepare wood accurately to size and for final cleaning, prior to using glasspaper
Taps and dies	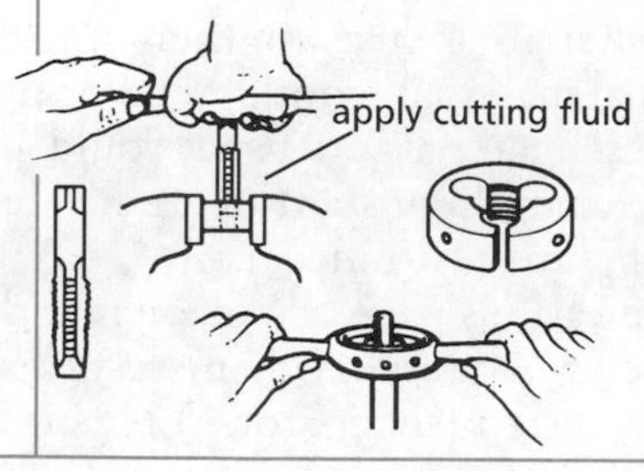 apply cutting fluid	W P	For cutting screw threads. Sizes range from 3 mm up to 15 mm and larger.

Key:
W = wood
P = plastics
M = metals

Fig. 6.1 Cutting and shaping tools

Tool	Tool in use	Use on	Notes
Files	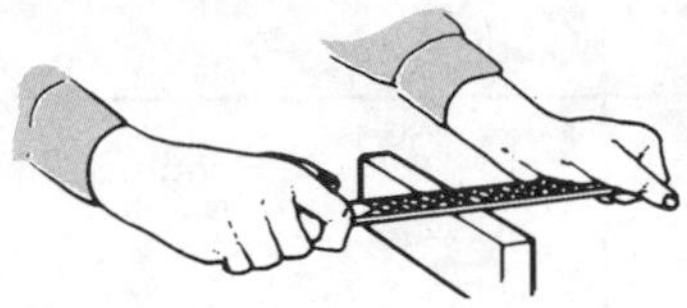	W M P	Available in a huge range of lengths, shapes and 'cuts'. Use on metals and plastics. If used on wood they tend to clog. Always make sure a handle is fitted.
Tin snips	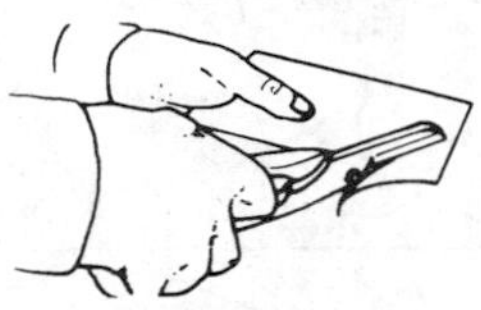	M P	Originally intended for cutting tin plate, but equally useful for sheet aluminium, copper, etc.' as well as sheet PVC and polystyrene
Side cutters	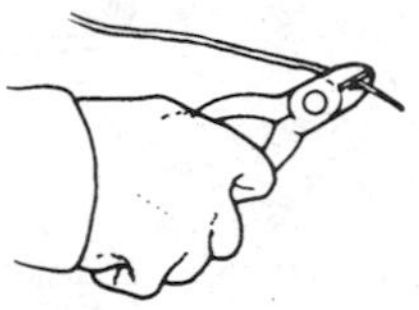	M	Used to snip off surplus wire after soldering electrical components. Can be used to cut electrical wire, but it should not be used to cut hard (piano) wire.
Acrylic cutter	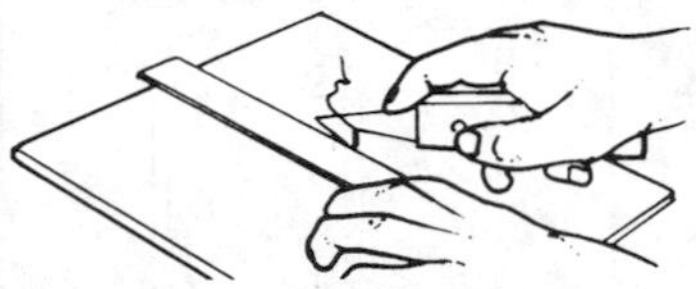	P	With this tool, the plastic (acrylic or polystyrene, for example) is scored and then broken along the line
Trimming knife	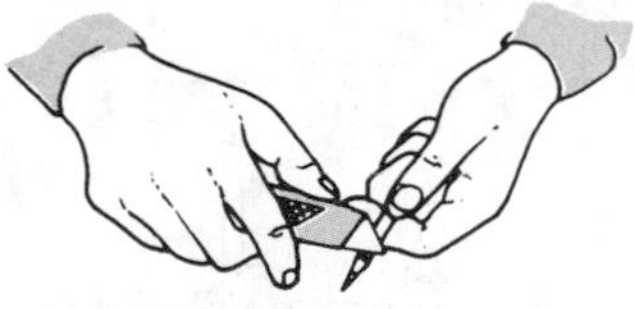	W P	Used for trimming paper, card, thin wood and plastics. It can also be used for accurate marking-out of wood.
Surform	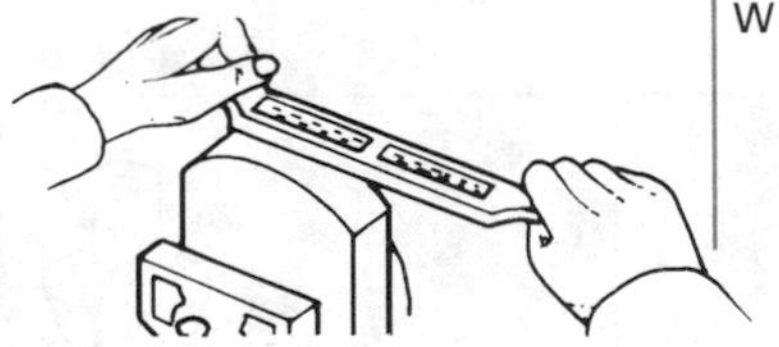	W	A very versatile tool for free shaping of wood, soft plastics, plaster, etc. Used with care, it can shape plastic foams, such as polyurethane.
Guillotine/ bench shear	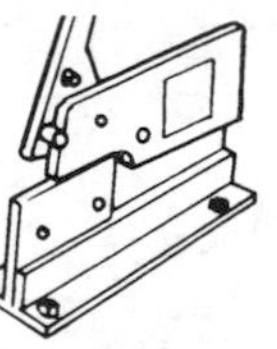	M P	For cutting sheet metal that cannot be cut with tin snips. It is usually locked closed when not in use, to avoid accidents
Hacksaw	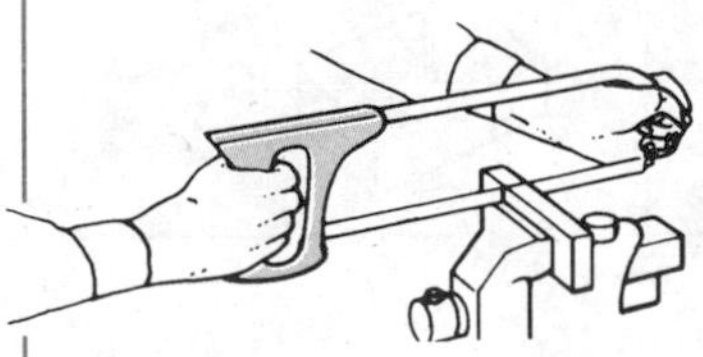	M P	For use on metals and plastics. The blade can be fitted sideways to allow cutting along the length of the material without the frame getting in the way.

Key:
W = wood
P = plastics
M = metals

Fig. 6.1 Cutting and shaping tools (continued)

Hole-making tools

Tool	Tool in use	Use on	Notes
Handdrill/ twist drills	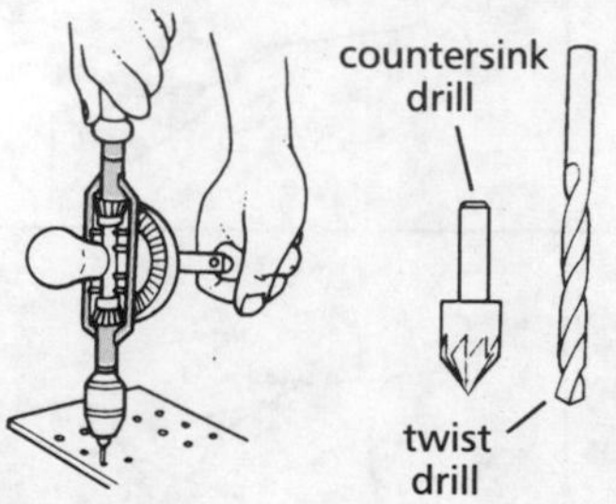 countersink drill / twist drill	W M	Difficult to use for large diameters
Brace/bits	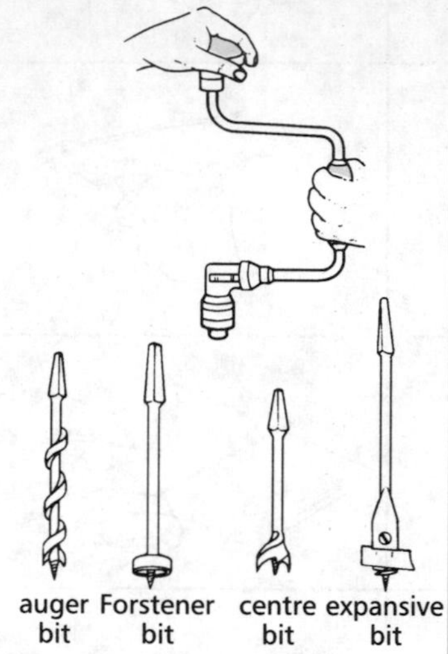 auger bit Forstener bit centre bit expansive bit	W	A wide range of bits are available for borong holes from 6 mm up to 50 mm diameter. Expansive (adjustable) bits can be used for larger holes.
Hole saw		W M P	Use with a pillar drill at slow speed. Good for making wheels.
Cone cut	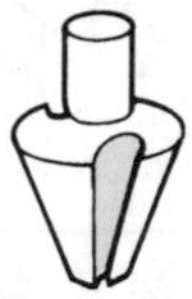	P	Useful for enlarging holes in sheet plastic and metal.
Bradawl	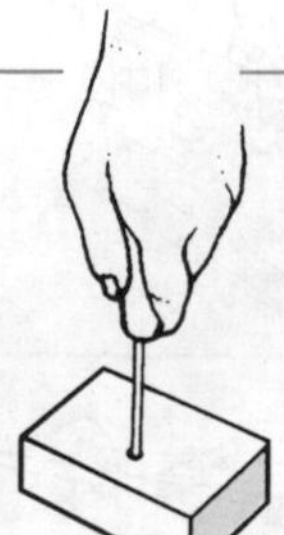	W P	For making small holes in timber and especially for 'starter' holes, prior to inserting woodscrews.

Key:
W = wood
P = plastics
M = metals

Fig. 6.2 Hole-making tools

Holding tools

Tool	Tool in use	Use on	Notes
G-cramp	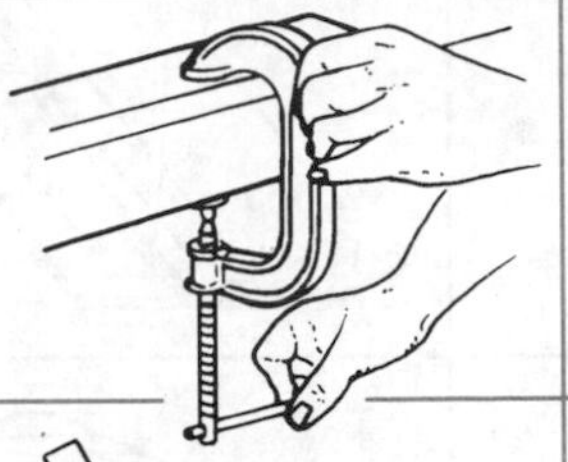	W M P	Used in almost all situations when two parts need to be held together for a short while, e.g., gluing up or drilling on the pillar drill
Toolmakaker's cramp		M P	For holding work together when a G-cramp is not appropriate. Usually used on small pieces of work and rarely with timber
Engineer's/ carpenter's vice	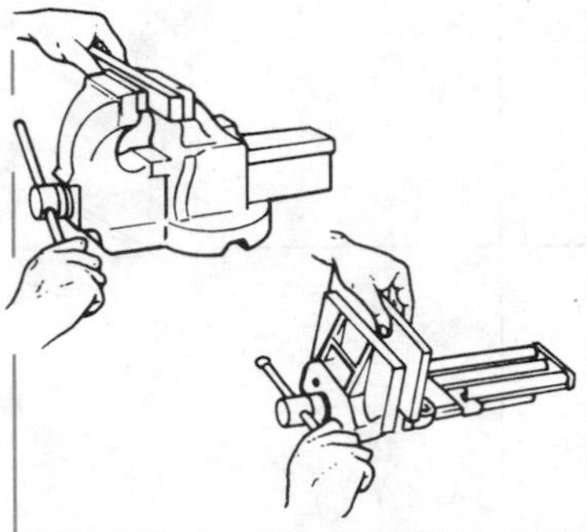	M P / W P	Remember: the engineer's vice has jaws that may damage soft materials. The carpenter's vice is better for holding large pieces of wood
Machine vice	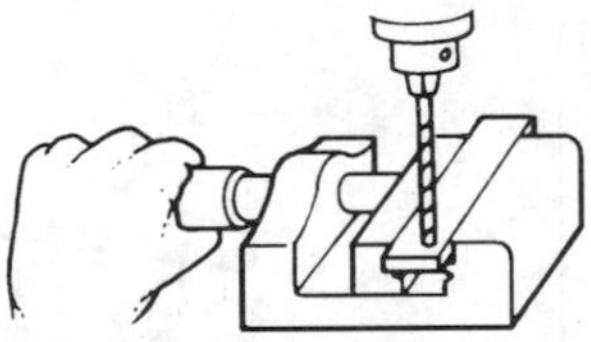	M P	Used to hold materials accurately and securely when drilling. The vice can either be hand held, bolted or cramped down.
Hand vice	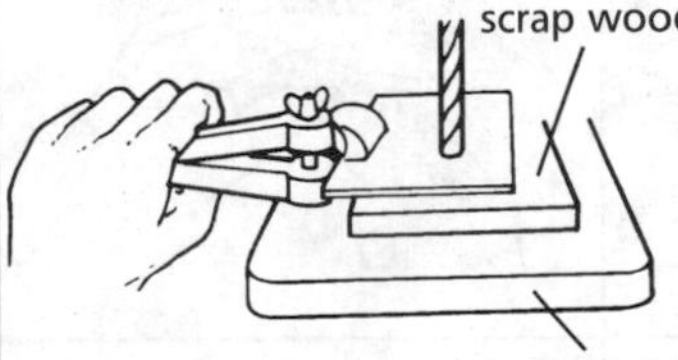 scrap wood / drill table	M P	Used to hold sheet materials when drilling. Make sure the wing nut is tight and hold securely in place
Pliers	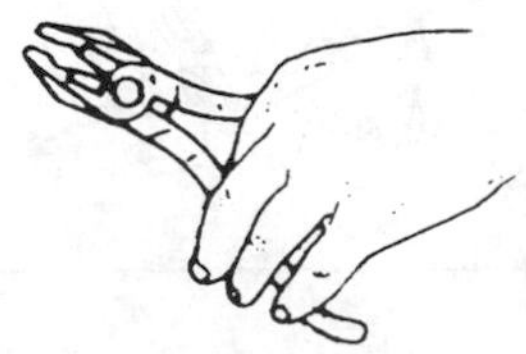	M P	Available in a variety of sizes. Used to hold small items when fingers would be too large or not strong enough. Do not use as a substitute for a spanner.

Key:
W = wood
P = plastics
M = metals

Fig. 6.3 Holding tools

Marking-out tools

Tool	Tool in use	Use on	Notes
Scriber	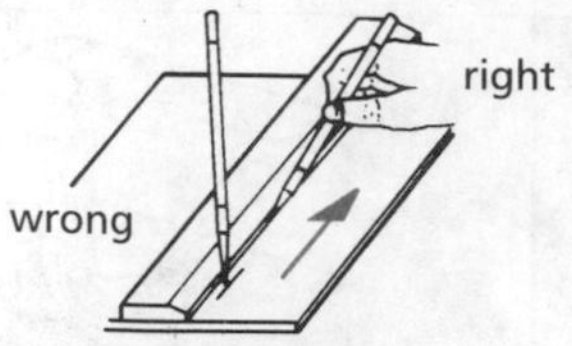 right / wrong	M P	Used to mark out on hard materials, such as metals
Engineer's square/ tri-square	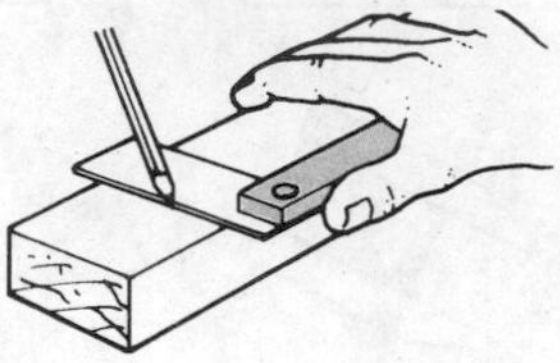	W M P	Marking line at right angles to the edge of metals, plastics and timber. Also used to check right angles
Dividers		M P	For transferring measurements and marking out arcs and circles on metals and plastics
Centre punch	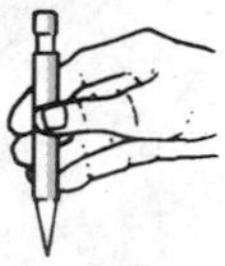	M P	Marking centres of holes before drilling or marking out with dividers.
Centre square		W M P	Used to find the centre of a round bar
Micrometer	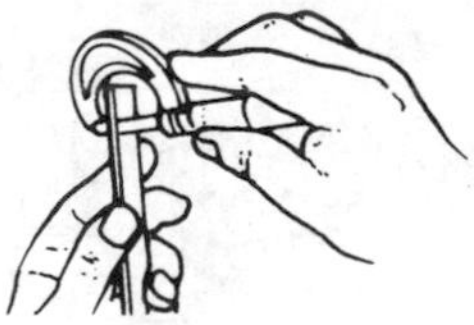	M P	Measuring and checking precise measurements. Cannot be used for internal measurements.
Sliding bevel	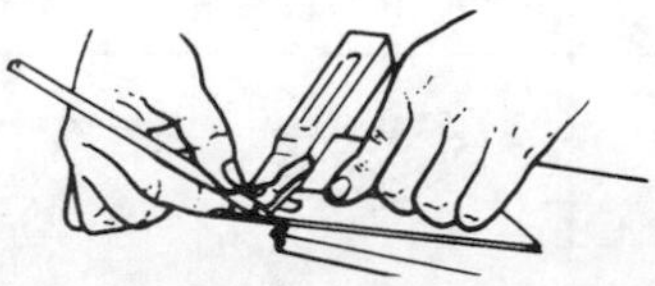	W M P	Marking out and copying of angles
Marking gauge	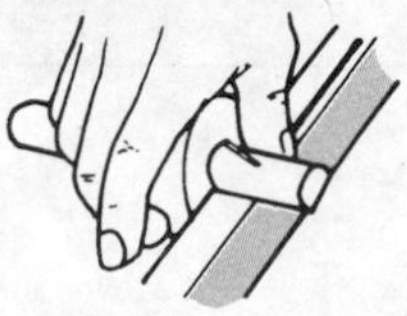	W P	Marking a line parallel to an edge.

Key:
W = wood
P = plastics
M = metals

Fig. 6.4 Marking-out tools

Machine tools

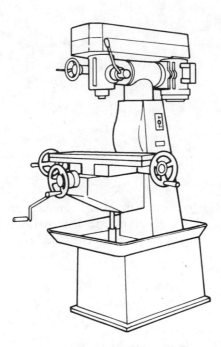

Fig. 6.5 Vertical milling machine

Milling machines are very adaptable machines which are designed to be used on metals and plastics. They produce flat surfaces, slots, angled surfaces, and accurately drilled holes. Computer numerical control (CNC) milling machines are found widely in schools and are used for cutting thin sheet metals and thermoplastics such as acrylic.

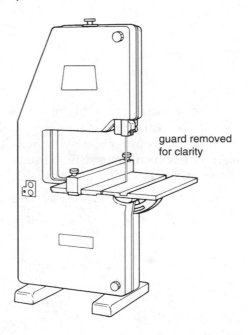

guard removed for clarity

Fig. 6.6 Band saw

The **band saw** is used widely for cutting curves and shapes in timber, plastics and metal (although a much finer blade is needed to cut metal).

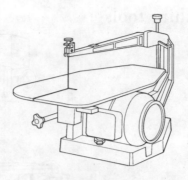

Fig. 6.7 Vibrating (or jig) saw

Vibrating (or jig) saw. This is an extremely useful tool for intricate work on thin sheet wood, metal and plastic. Internal shapes can be cut easily by first drilling a small hole in the work and passing the blade through the hole before securing it in the saw.

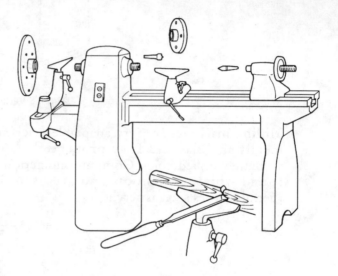

Fig. 6.8 Wood-turning lathe

Wood-turning lathe. This machine tool is used for turning circular objects in wood. The cutting tools (chisels) are held firmly by the operator and the diameter of the wood is progressively turned down. The work is either held on a small face plate or between centres. Wood turning lathes are computer controlled in industry where products such as identical chair legs are made in vast quantities.

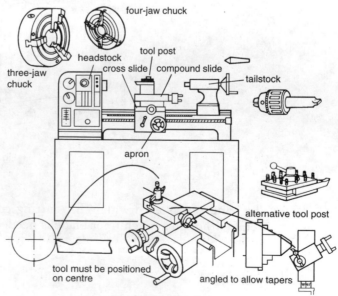

Fig. 6.9 Centre lathe

Centre lathe (or metalwork lathe) is a versatile machine used for turning circular objects in metal and plastic. The work is normally held in a chuck and supported if necessary. Centre lathes are almost all computerised in industry when used for production. CNC lathes are controlled by a computer program which sends a code to the lathe for each operation.

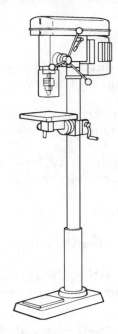

Fig. 6.10 Pillar drilling machine

The pillar drill. When drilling holes it is essential that the work is securely clamped in position. This is particularly important when drilling thin sheet metal which can easily grip and spin if not secured. A particular hazard when drilling metal comes from the swarf (small sharp coils of metal) which is frequently very hot and can burn the hands and face.

6.2 Materials

Properties of materials

All resistant materials have physical and mechanical properties which make them ideally suited for particular products. The properties required of a product should be detailed in the design specification; this will help you to choose the most appropriate materials for a design.

The main properties are:

Mechanical properties

Strength: the ability of a material to withstand an applied force.

Hardness: a measure of how easily a material is scratched or damaged – very hard materials like glass or cast iron are often brittle (they have low impact resistance).

Toughness: how well a material resists impact.

Stiffness: the ability to resist bending .

Ductility: the ability of a material to be worked – ductile materials can be formed easily into shapes, e.g. pressing deep shapes in steel such as car body panels.

Compression: the ability to withstand squeezing forces.

Tension: the ability to withstand pulling forces.

Physical properties

Thermal conductivity: how well a material conducts heat – e.g. aluminium is a very good conductor of heat.

Resistance to corrosion: how easily the material oxidises – ferrous metals have a very low resistance to corrosion.

Electrical conductivity: how well the material conducts electricity – copper is a very good conductor, materials that do not conduct are called insulators.

Optical properties: how easily light passes through the material.

Appearance: related to aesthetics, colour, brightness, texture of the material.

Joining properties: the ability of the material to be joined to itself and other materials – some woods, e.g. teak, are very oily and do not glue well.

Selecting the best material

Apart from the physical and mechanical properties of materials you should also consider cost, availability (how easy is it to get hold of the material in the size you want it), available tools and equipment and the stock size. **All these are important considerations.**

Metals

Ferrous metals

The word **ferrous** comes from the Latin word for iron. Ferrous metals contain iron; they are almost all magnetic and unless treated, rust very easily.

Material	Uses	Notes
Cast iron	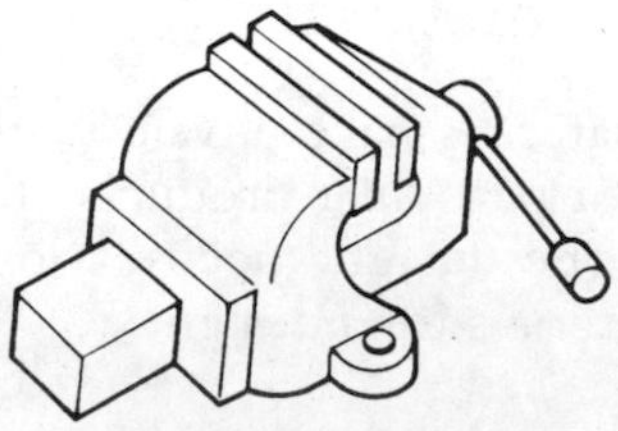	Hard skin. Strong under compression. Cannot be bent or forged
Mild steel		Tough, ductile and malleable . Easily joined but with poor resistance to corrosion. Cannot be hardened or tempered.

Fig. 6.11 Ferrous metals

E **xaminer's tip**

Make sure you know the properties of common woods, metals and plastics.

Material	Uses	Notes
High-carbon steel	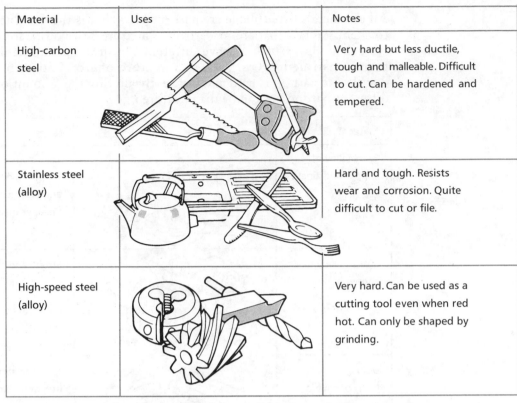	Very hard but less ductile, tough and malleable. Difficult to cut. Can be hardened and tempered.
Stainless steel (alloy)		Hard and tough. Resists wear and corrosion. Quite difficult to cut or file.
High-speed steel (alloy)		Very hard. Can be used as a cutting tool even when red hot. Can only be shaped by grinding.

Fig. 6.11 Ferrous metals (continued)

Non-ferrous metals

These metals do not contain iron. The most common examples of pure non-ferrous metals are copper, aluminium, tin and lead. Because they do not contain iron they do not rust (oxidise).

Material	Uses	Notes
Aluminium		High strength/weight ratio. Difficult to join. Good conductor of heat and electricity Corrosion resistant. Polishes well.
Copper	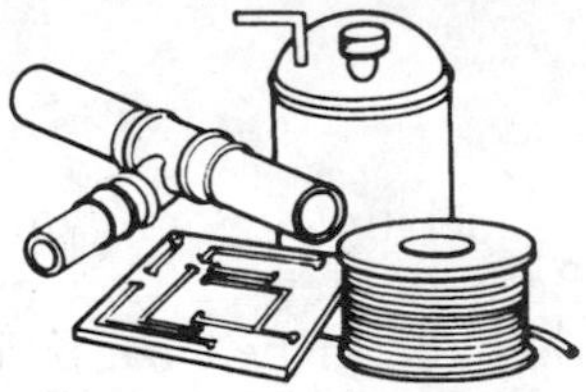	Malleable and ductile. Good conductor of heat and electricity Easily joined. Polishes well. Expensive.
Lead	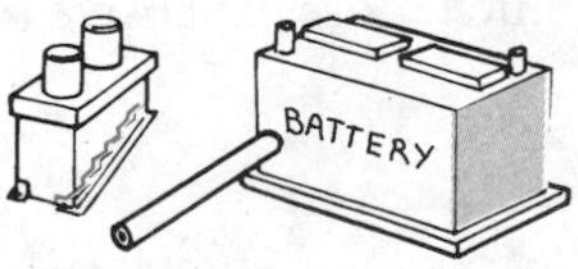	Very heavy, soft, malleable and ductile. Corrosion resistant. Low melting point. Difficult to work and expensive.
Tin (tin plate)		Soft and weak. Ductile and malleable. High corrosion resistance. Low melting point. Used to coat steel to produce 'tin plate'.

Fig. 6.12 Non-ferrous metals

All the metals listed above are pure metals – that is there are no other metals added to them. Metals that are made from a mixture of two or more metals or elements are called alloys. Alloys have different physical and mechanical properties from their constituent parts. Steel is a mixture of iron and carbon. Iron is soft and ductile and carbon is hard and brittle. By altering the amount of carbon, steels with different hardnesses can be manufactured.

Material	Uses	Notes
Brass (alloy of copper and zinc)		Corrosion resistant. Harder than copper. Good conductor of heat and electricity. Polishes well. Cheaper than copper.
Bronze (alloy of copper and tin)		Strong and tough. Corrosion resistant. Resistant to wearing.
Duralumin (alloy of several metals and a non-metal)		Nearly as strong as mild steel, but much lighter. Hardens with age. Machines well after annealing.

Fig. 6.13 Alloys

Timber

There are two different types of natural timber: hardwood and softwood. Softwood comes from trees that are cone bearing (coniferous), have needles and are evergreen (they do not lose their leaves in the winter). Hardwoods come from trees that carry their seeds in fruit, they are broad leaved and nearly always deciduous (they lose their leaves in winter). Be careful! Although most hardwoods are hard, there are one or two exceptions to this. Balsa wood, for example, is a hardwood.

Hardwoods

Hardwoods are generally slow growing and take many years to mature (typically 60–100 years). Because they are slow growing, the growth rings (annular rings) are very close together and make what is termed 'close-grained' timber. Close-grained timbers are usually strong and tough. However, because they are slow growing, hardwoods are much more expensive to buy.

Softwoods

These come from trees commonly referred to as pine. They are fast growing, maturing in about 20–30 years. This makes them ideal for commercial growing. Softwoods are used extensively for making paper. Because they are fast growing, the growth rings (annular rings) are quite widely spaced or 'open grained'. Open-grained timber is less strong than close grained and splits easily. Softwoods are much cheaper to buy because they grow very quickly and are very tall and straight, which means there is little waste when they are cut. A word of warning, softwoods such as Yew are harder than many hardwoods.

Natural timbers have a number of drawbacks:

- they suffer from moisture – they warp and twist if they are not properly seasoned (dried)
- they are relatively expensive to buy
- they do not come in large sizes (for example, several pieces need to be joined to make a table top)

Fixing	Uses	Notes
Mahogany		Easy to work. Fairly strong. Durable. Prone to warping.
Beech	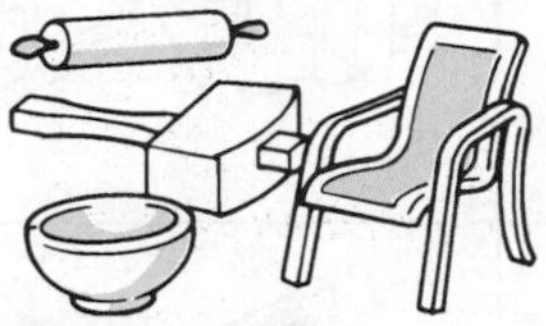	Close-grained, hard, tough and strong. Works and finishes well. Prone to warping.
Ash		Open-grained, tough and flexible. Good elastic qualities. Works well.
Oak		Very strong, heavy and durable Hard and tough. Open-grained. Contains tannic acid, which corrodes iron and steel.
Teak		Hard, very strong and very durable. Very resistant to acids and alkalis. Contains grit, which blunts tools easily. Very expensive.
Jelutong	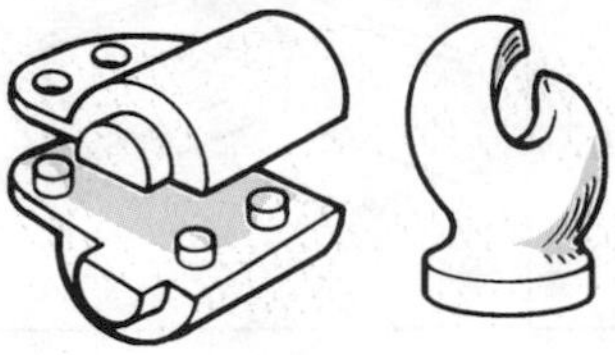	Pale cream in colour. Uniform grain. Shapes easily. Very few knots.
Balsa		Very soft and light. Ideal for models. Quite expensive.

Fig. 6.14 Hardwoods

Material	Uses	Notes
Scots pine	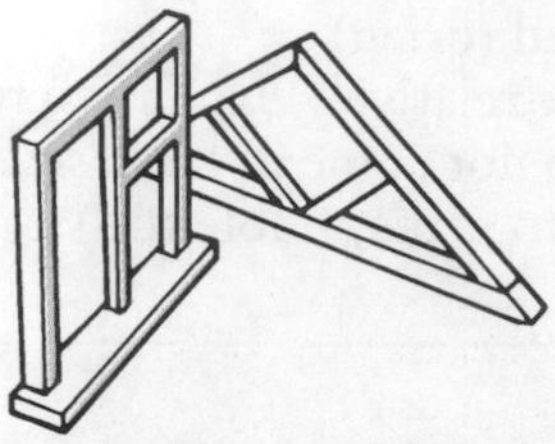	Straight-grained but knotty. Fairly strong, easy to work and cheap. Readily available
Spruce	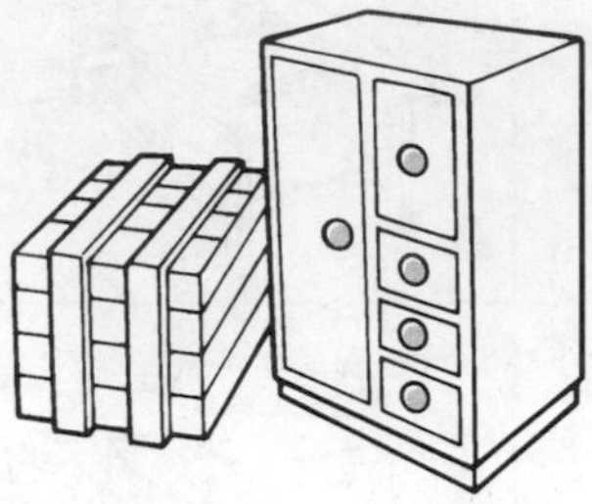	Fairly strong. Small hard knots. Resistant to splitting. Not durable.
Douglas fir		Dark red/brown. Fairly durable and quite dense.
Western red cedar		Lightweight, knot-free, soft, straight silky grain. Durable against weather, insects and rotting. Easy to work but expensive.
Parana pine	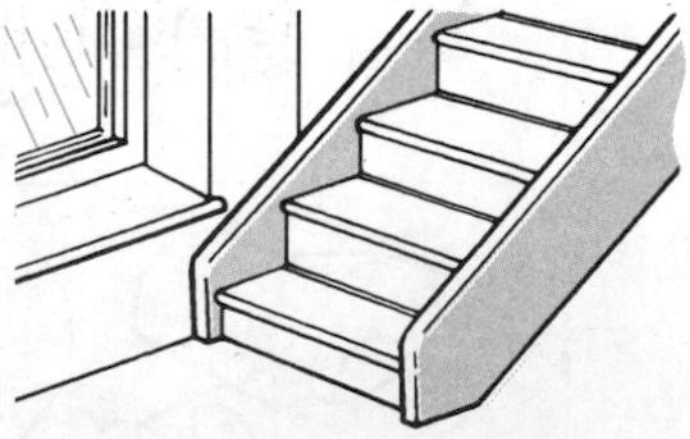	Hard, straight-grained. Almost knot-free. Strong and durable Tends to warp. Expensive for softwood. Used for internal joinery.

Fig. 6.15 Softwoods

Manufactured boards

These are completely the opposite to natural timbers; they are made in large sizes (up to 3 metres × 2 metres). They are relatively cheap and, because they do not have a grain running through them, they do not warp and twist in the same way as natural timbers.

Material	Thickness available	Uses	Notes
Hardboard	3.2 mm 6 mm	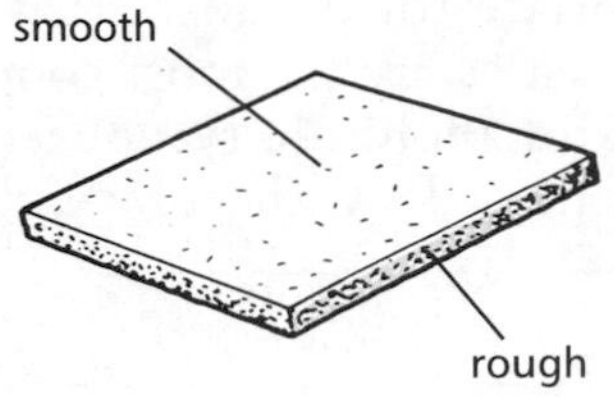 smooth / rough	Cheap and fairly light. Used as a substitute for plywood. No grain. Equally strong in all directions. Standard hardboard absorbs moisture and must not be used outdoors. Usually smooth on one side only.
Veneers	1 mm 2 mm 3 mm	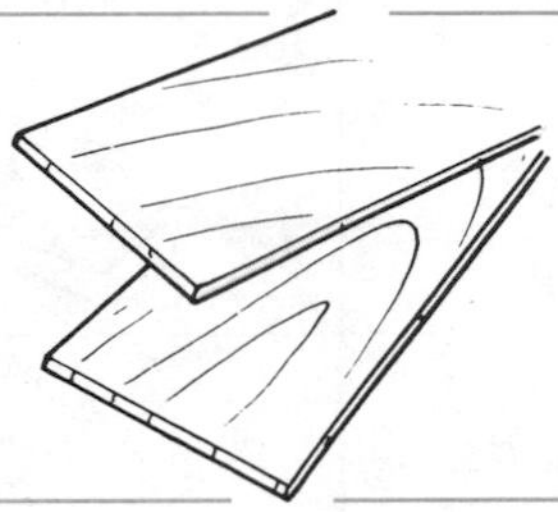	Thin layers of wood. Used for making plywood or laminating. A very economical use of timber, since very little of the tree is wasted.
Plywood	3 mm, 4 mm 6 mm, 8 mm 10 mm, 12 mm 15 mm, 18 mm	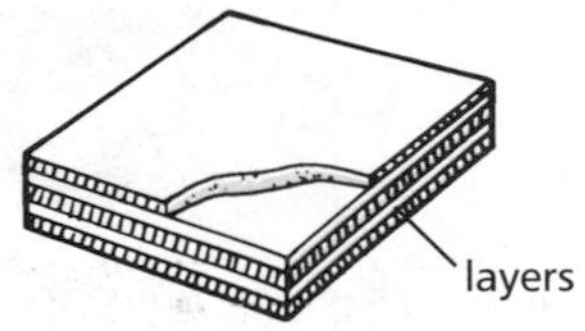 layers	Made from veneers of birch, alder, meranti or gaboon. Odd number of layers. Fairly cheap. Much stronger than hardboard. Some forms of plywood resistant to moisture.
Blockboard and laminboard	12 mm 15 mm 18 mm	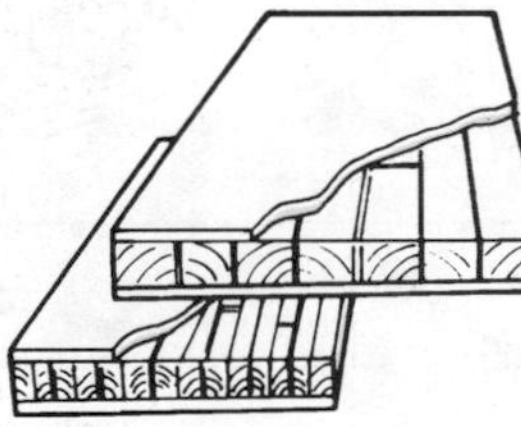	Cheaper to make, thickness-for-thickness, than plywood, although not the same uniform strength.
Chipboard	12 mm 15 mm 18 mm		Chips of variety of timbers are bonded using synthetic glue. Available veneered with timber or plastic and used for cheaper, often 'flat pack', furniture.
Medium density fibreboard (MDF)	6 mm 12 mm 15 mm 18 mm	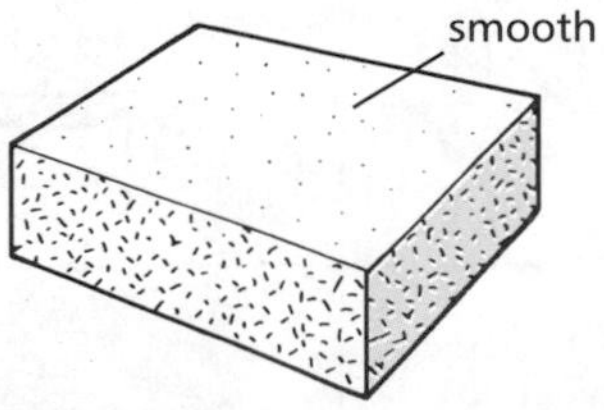 smooth	A sort of thicker, smoother, better quality hardboard. Has smooth faces and takes paint well.

Fig. 6.16 Manufactured boards

Plastics (proper name, synthetic polymers)

There are two main types of plastic: **thermoplastics and thermosetting plastics.**

Thermoplastics

Thermoplastics have what is termed 'plastic memory'; that is when they are heated they soften and return to their original shape (usually a flat sheet). This can be tested by bending an old phone card or bank card in half, placing it in a bowl and pouring boiling water over it; it will return to its flat shape. Thermoplastics generally soften at low temperature (as low as 100 °C). This makes them inappropriate for products that involve relatively high temperatures. However, thermoplastics are the most common type of plastic and are widely used. In your design and technology course you will have formed acrylic and probably polystyrene or PVC sheet by vacuum forming.

Material	Uses	Notes
Acrylic (PMMA)		Stiff, hard and uniform strength. Scratches easily. Clear; has good optical properties. Non-toxic. Good insulator, easily machined and polishes well.
Rigid polystyrene (PS)	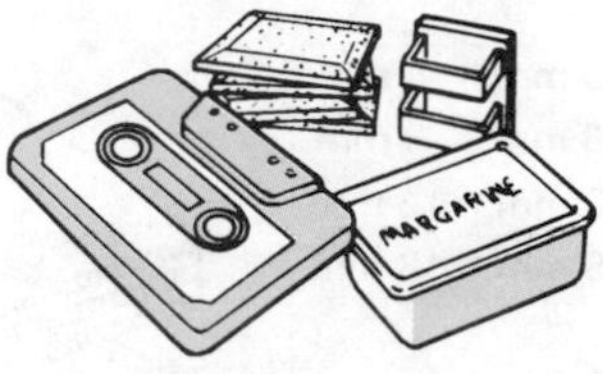	Light, hard, stiff, often transparent. Brittle with low impact strength. Water resistant. The toughened type can be coloured.
Expanded polystyrene (PS)		Buoyant, lightweight. A good sound and heat insulator.
Polyamide (nylon)		Usually creamy in colour. Hard, tough and resistant to wear. Low friction. Machines well, but very difficult to join.
Polyethylene (polythene, PE)		Tough, very popular. Quite cheap. Available in a wide range of colours. Fairly low melting point.
Acrylonitrile butadienestyrene (ABS)	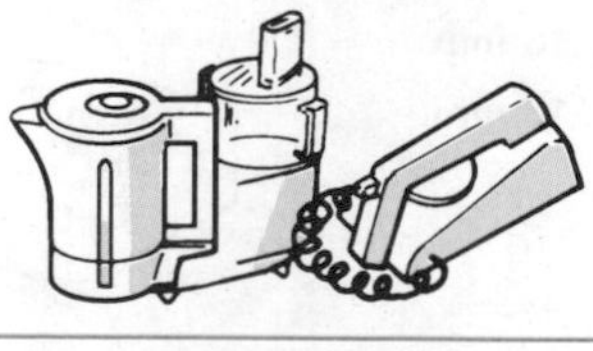	High impact strength. Tough and scratch resistant. Resistant to chemicals.
Polyvinyl chloride (PVC)		Chemical and weather resistant. Wide range of colours. Needs a stabiliser for outdoor use. Good electrical insulator.
Polyethylene terephthalate (PET)		Used extensively for mineral water bottles. Clear and very tough.

Fig. 6.17 Thermoplastics

Thermosetting plastics (thermosets)

These are quite different from thermoplastics. When they are being formed a chemical reaction occurs causing them to create strong links or cross chains in their structure, which means once set they are permanently formed (they cannot be softened). Because they do not soften when heated they can take very high temperatures often in excess of 400 °C. Imagine if kitchen worktops were made from a thermoplastic – what would happen when a hot frying pan was placed on one?

Certain thermosets such as polyester resin (GRP or fibreglass) as well as adhesives such as Araldite, which is an epoxy resin, are used within design and technology courses. The two most common thermosets in the home are urea formaldehyde (used for electrical fittings) and melamine formaldehyde (e.g. kitchen worktops and 'unbreakable plates').

Material	Uses	Notes
Polyester resin (GRP)		Stiff, hard and brittle. Used for casting and, when reinforced by glass fibres, produces GRP. Easy to colour. Excellent for outdoor uses.
Urea formaldehyde (UF)		Stiff, hard and brittle. Excellent electrical insulator. Used as an adhesive.
Epoxy resin		Very strong, especially when reinforced by glass or carbon fibres. Used as an adhesive for unlike materials.
Melamine formaldehyde (MF)		Stiff, hard and strong. Scratch resistant. Low water absorption. Stain resistant. No odour. Available in a wide range of colours.

Fig. 6.18 Thermosets

Market forms

When selecting appropriate materials, one consideration is the standard sizes or stock sizes that materials are manufactured in.

Timber

Timber is mostly sold by length although large planks are often sold by the square metre.

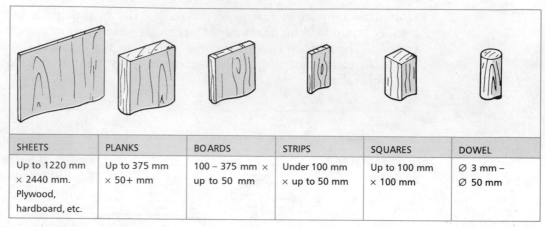

SHEETS	PLANKS	BOARDS	STRIPS	SQUARES	DOWEL
Up to 1220 mm × 2440 mm. Plywood, hardboard, etc.	Up to 375 mm × 50+ mm	100 – 375 mm × up to 50 mm	Under 100 mm × up to 50 mm	Up to 100 mm × 100 mm	∅ 3 mm – ∅ 50 mm

Metals

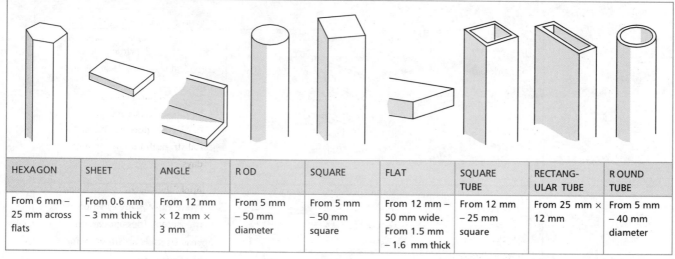

HEXAGON	SHEET	ANGLE	ROD	SQUARE	FLAT	SQUARE TUBE	RECTANG-ULAR TUBE	ROUND TUBE
From 6 mm – 25 mm across flats	From 0.6 mm – 3 mm thick	From 12 mm × 12 mm × 3 mm	From 5 mm – 50 mm diameter	From 5 mm – 50 mm square	From 12 mm – 50 mm wide. From 1.5 mm – 1.6 mm thick	From 12 mm – 25 mm square	From 25 mm × 12 mm	From 5 mm – 40 mm diameter

Plastics

	POWDER	GRANULES	FOAM	FILM	SHEET	BLOCK	HEXAGONAL BAR	RODS	TUBES	RESINS AND PASTES
Polyethylene (PE)	✓	✓	✗	✓	✗	✗	✗	✗	✓	✗
Acrylic (PMMA)	✗	✓	✗	✗	✓	✓	✗	✓	✓	✓
Nylon	✓	✓	✗	✗	✗	✓	✓	✓	✓	✗
PVC	✓	✓	✗	✗	✓	✗	✗	✗	✓	✗
Polystyrene (PS)	✓	✓	✓	✗	✓	✓	✗	✗	✗	✗
Polyester	✗	✗	✓	✗	✗	✗	✗	✗	✗	✓
Epoxy	✗	✗	✗	✗	✗	✗	✗	✗	✗	✓

✓ Readily available   ✗ Not readily available

Fig 6.19 Market forms

6.3 Joining

Adhesives

When selecting the joining methods for your designed products, you need to ensure that you choose the most appropriate adhesive. There are many different adhesives and your choice will depend on the type of material to be glued, the strength needed and the environment that the product will work in (e.g. PVA wood glue is water soluble, therefore it cannot be used outdoors).

Adhesive	Uses	Hints on use	Setting time	Pressure
Polyvinyl acetate (PVA) / Evostik resin W	Used mainly for timber and paper products.	Not always waterproof. Wipe off excess before it dries.	Long setting time (several hours)	Sustained pressure is needed
Synthetic resin / Cascamite / Aerolite 306	Stronger than PVA and also waterproof.	Chemically active. Needs mixing with water. Will fill small gaps in a joint.		
Acrylic cement / Tensol 12	Used only for acrylic. It does not work with other plastics or other materials.	Ensure good ventilation. Replace cap when not in use.		Usually only hand pressure is needed
Epoxy resin / Araldite	Expensive but versatile. Will bond almost any clean material.	Resin and hardener need to be mixed. It hardens quite quickly but does not reach full strength for two to three days.	Short setting time (less than one hour)	
Contact adhesive / Evostik Contact / Thixofix (Dunlop)	Used mainly for gluing sheet material, such as melamine to work surfaces.	Apply thin layers to each side. Allow to dry. Adhesion occurs on contact. The vapours are harmful and ventilation is essential.		
Latex adhesive / Copydex	Suitable for fabrics, paper and upholstery.	Non-toxic and safe for young children to use.		
Polystyrene cement / Airfix cement	Used only on rigid polystyrene (expanded polystyrene will melt).	Ensure good ventilation.		
Rubber solution / Bostik	Used only for rubber, especially in bicycle puncture repairs.	Read the manufacturer's instructions carefully.		
Glue gun	Used for rapid gluing of small pieces.	Take care, as the glue is used hot and can burn the skin badly.		

Table 6.1 Adhesives

Soldering and welding metals

Although permanent joints in metal can be made using adhesives, it is far more common to solder or weld joints. Both of these processes involve heat and the addition of a second metal which melts to form the joint.

Soldering

There are two main types: **soft** soldering and **hard** soldering. Soft soldering is used for attaching (soldering) electronic components to a board and joining thin plate. It uses a solder (the name given to the filler metal) made from lead and tin. Lead/tin solder has a very low melting point. Hard soldering (brazing and silver soldering) produces much stronger joints than soft soldering and requires much more heat to melt the solder.

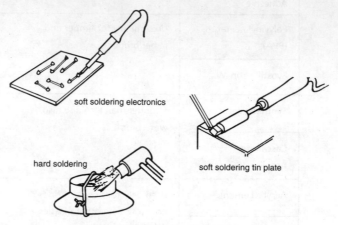

Fig. 6.20 Soldering techniques

Welding

This process involves much greater heat than soldering and is usually provided by an oxygen/acetylene torch. The gap between the two surfaces is filled by a filler rod of the same material. Steel is often welded by an electric welding machine called an arc welder. With arc welders a very high current causes an arc between the rod and the metal to be joined (with is connected to earth). The heat from the arc melts the metal and fuses the joint together. Plastic can also be welded using heat (around 400 °C). Heat welding is used for sealing polythene packaging.

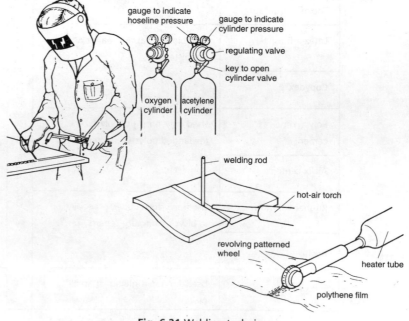

Fig. 6.21 Welding techniques

Joining wood

There are many ways of permanently joining wood. The choice of joint depends on the *function* of the product being constructed. The three main reasons for using construction joints are:

Strength: many joints 'lock' the two pieces of wood together when well produced, e.g. a dovetail joint. This is particularly important when certain forces act upon a joint such as compression, shear and tension. The strength of a glued joint depends largely upon the size of the glueing area – cutting a joint increases the amount of wood in contact.

Appearance: many construction joints look good and contribute to the aesthetics of the design.

Quality: because of strength and appearance they add quality to a product.

Examiner's tip

Take time to examine a wide range of furniture products – look for examples of these joints.

Name	Joint	Advantages/disadvantages
Butt	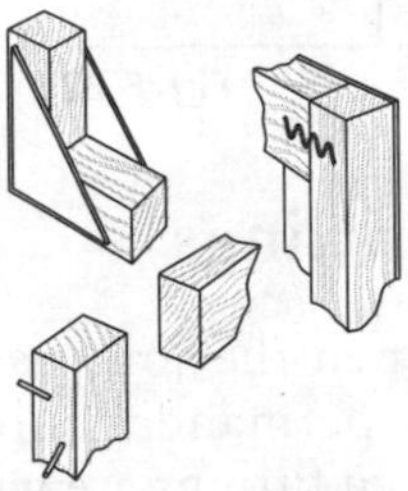	Simple, very little preparation needed. Low strength.
Mitre	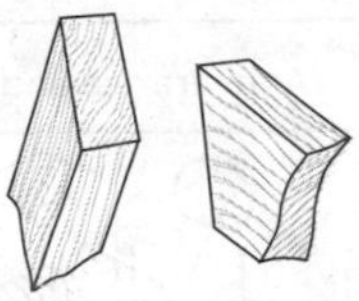	Attractive, often used as a decorative corner joint, hides the end grain. Low strength. Harder to make than the butt as it involves cutting the edges accurately at 45 °.
Dowelled joints	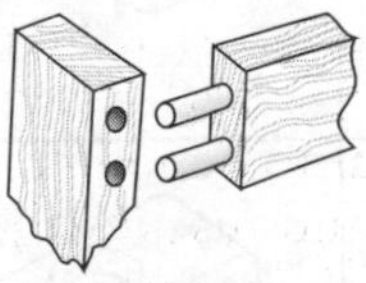	Neat and strong. The holes for the dowels must be lined up extremely accurately – this can be done with the help of a dowelling jig.
Corner halving	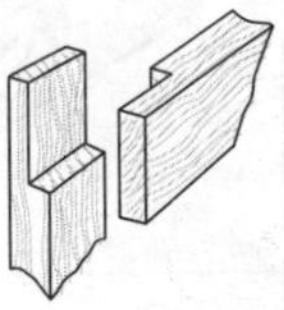	Relatively strong and quite easy to make. Usually needs strengthening with either screws or a dowel.
Mortise and tenon	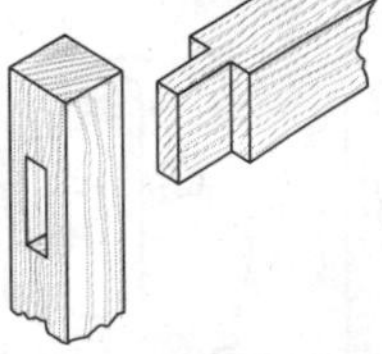	The strongest and most important joint used in frame construction. Used for strength in doors and furniture.
Dovetail joint	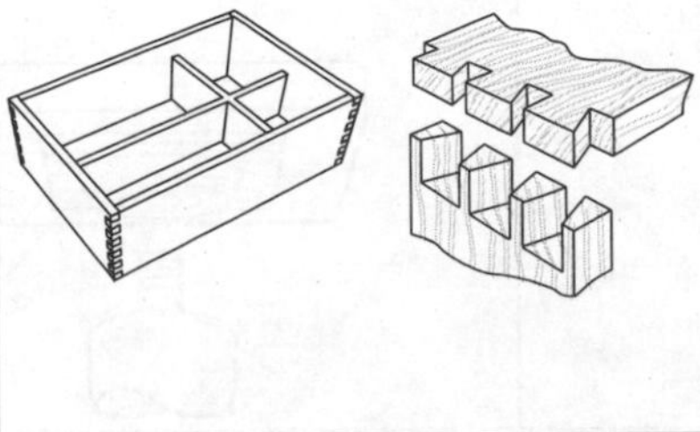	The strongest corner joints, they have a large glueing area and they lock the two pieces together and can only be pulled apart in one direction. Although difficult to make they look very attractive and are often found on quality furniture.

Fig. 6.22 Types of wood joint

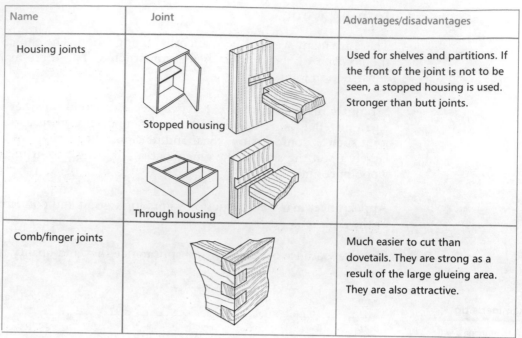

Name	Joint	Advantages/disadvantages
Housing joints	Stopped housing Through housing	Used for shelves and partitions. If the front of the joint is not to be seen, a stopped housing is used. Stronger than butt joints.
Comb/finger joints		Much easier to cut than dovetails. They are strong as a result of the large glueing area. They are also attractive.

Fig. 6.22 Types of wood joint (continued)

Knock-down fittings

These are used when the joint is temporary, semi-permanent or the material is inappropriate for permanent jointing (e.g. plywood and chipboard split very easily). Knock-down fittings are widely used in self-assembly furniture.

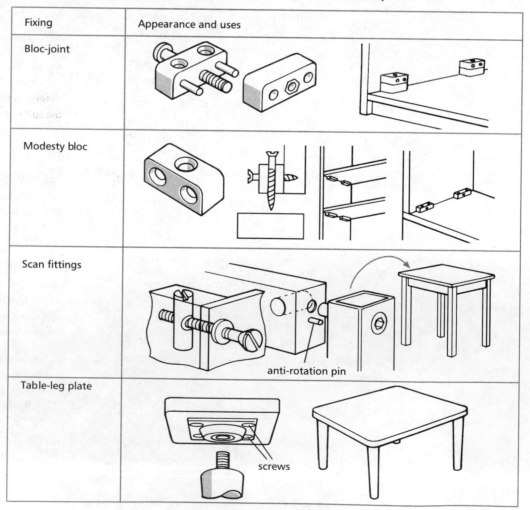

Fixing	Appearance and uses
Bloc-joint	
Modesty bloc	
Scan fittings	anti-rotation pin
Table-leg plate	screws

Fig. 6.23 Knock-down fittings

Fixing	Appearance and uses
Disc and peg	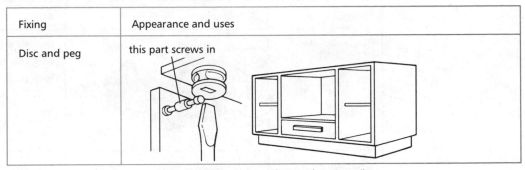 this part screws in

Fig. 6.23 Knock-down fittings (continued)

Mechanical fixings

These are normally used for semi-permanent or temporary joining. There is a wide variety and each has a particular use.

Fixing	Appearance	Uses
Round wire nail	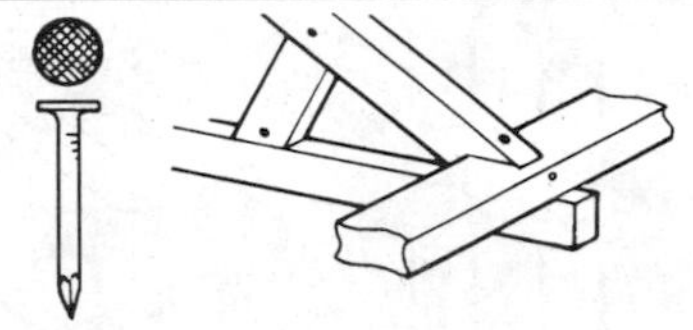	General purpose nail. Do not use near end of timber or timber will split.
Oval wire nail	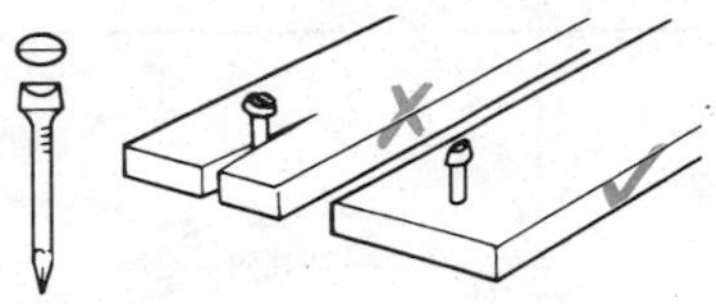	Similar use to round wire nail, but less likely to split wood if used correctly. More likely to bend.
Hardboard nail	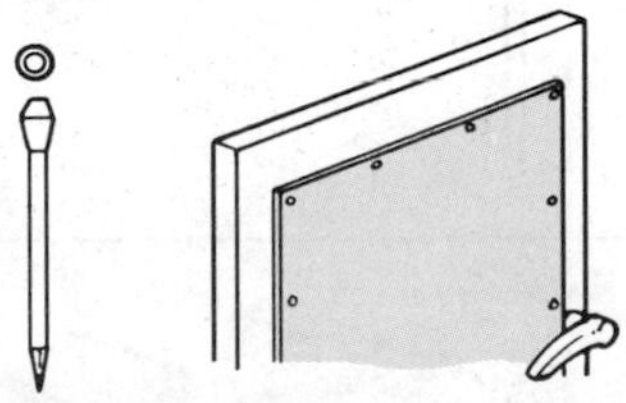	Designed to fix panels of hardboard. The head is shaped so that it sinks into the surface.
Masonry nail	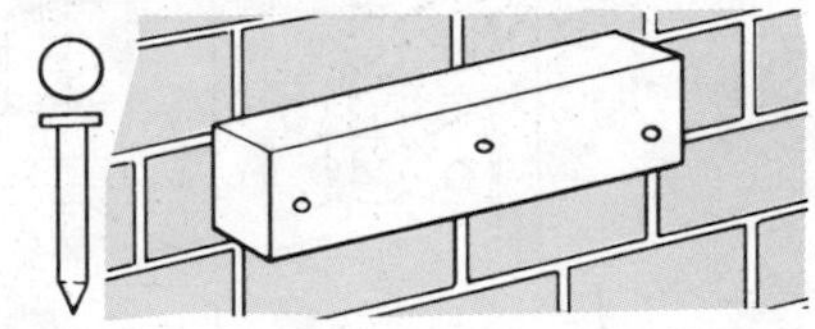	Useful for quick (and sometimes crude) fixing to brick, concrete and block walls.
Countersunk woodscrew	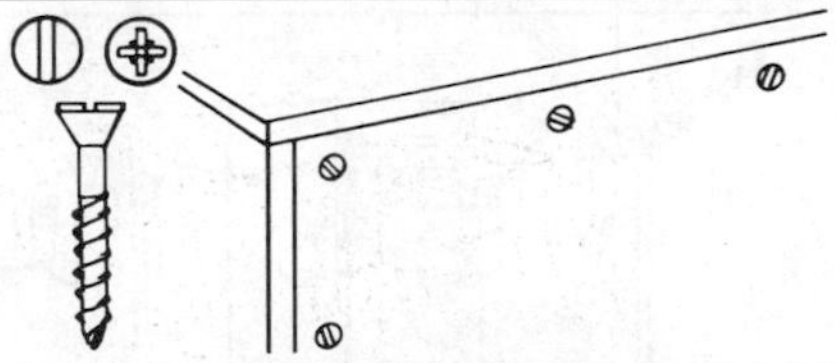	Usually with a slotted or cross-point head. Used to fix two pieces together. Make sure the piece nearest to the head has clearance-size hole drilled.
Round-head woodscrew	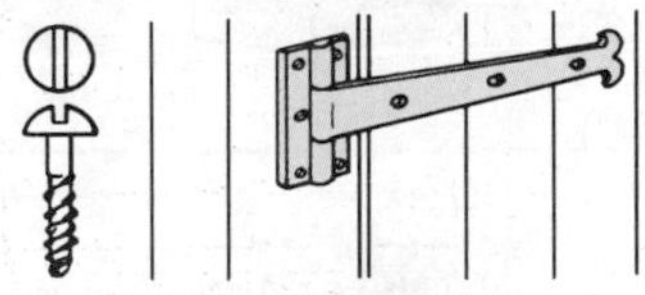	For holding panels of thin material or where it is not possible to make a counter sink.
Clout nail		For holding roof felt. Galvanized for outdoor use

Fig. 6.24 Mechanical fixings

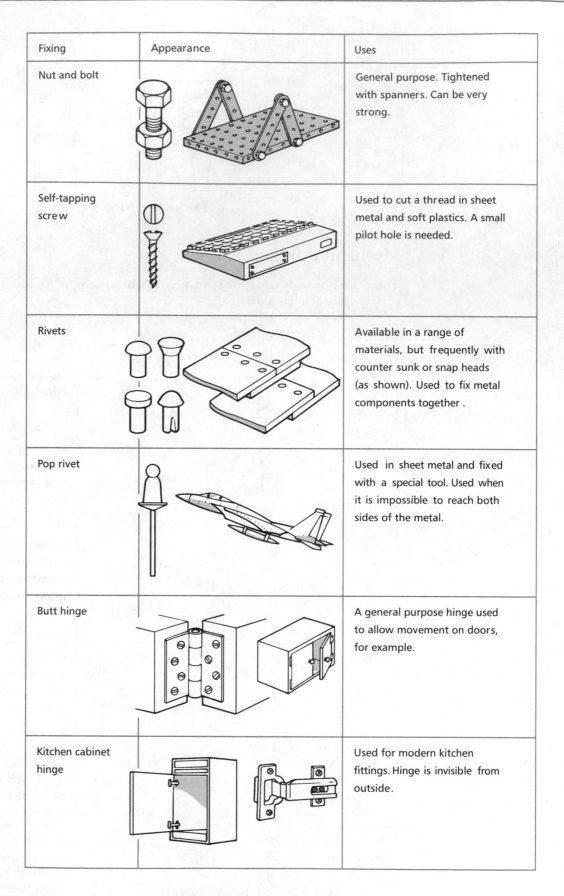

Fixing	Appearance	Uses
Nut and bolt		General purpose. Tightened with spanners. Can be very strong.
Self-tapping screw		Used to cut a thread in sheet metal and soft plastics. A small pilot hole is needed.
Rivets		Available in a range of materials, but frequently with counter sunk or snap heads (as shown). Used to fix metal components together.
Pop rivet		Used in sheet metal and fixed with a special tool. Used when it is impossible to reach both sides of the metal.
Butt hinge		A general purpose hinge used to allow movement on doors, for example.
Kitchen cabinet hinge		Used for modern kitchen fittings. Hinge is invisible from outside.

Fig. 6.24 Mechanical fixings (continued)

6.4 Surface finishes

The surface finish you apply to resistant materials has a substantial effect upon the quality of the product. Surface finishes or treatments have both a functional and an aesthetic aspect.

Function: to protect the product – this could be to prevent oxidisation, scratching or tarnishing.

Aesthetics: colour can create an image or style, it can imbue a sense of quality, make a product look heavy, light or even stand out.

The required finish for a product will be identified in the product design specification. Before choosing an appropriate surface finish there are five things to consider:

- the type of material
- the function of the finish
- how it is going to be applied
- the skill of the person applying the finish
- the cost

Finish	Uses	Notes
Paint and primer		Take care to prepare surface Remove rust or old paint before applying primer
Cellulose paint	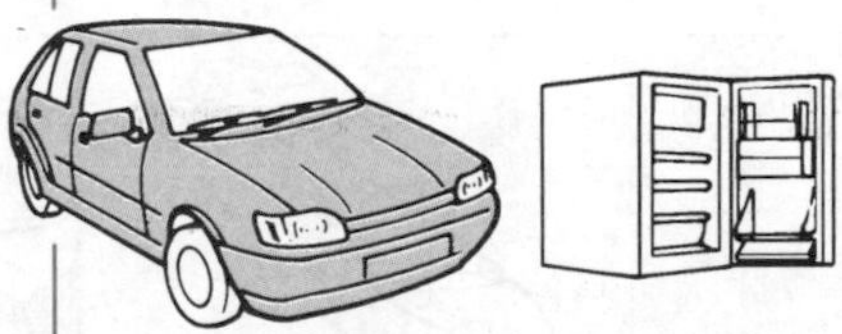	Usually sprayed with specialist equipment. Care must be taken to avoid breathing fumes.
Lacquer	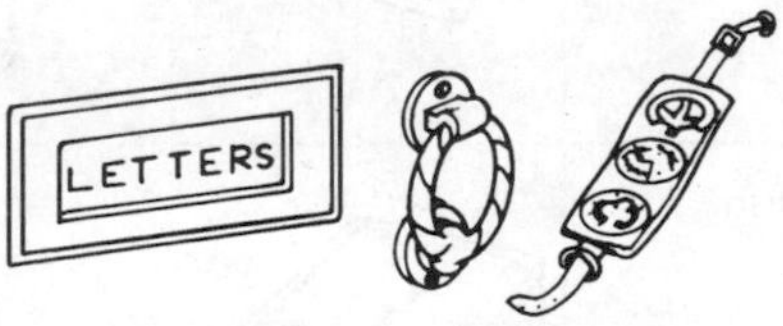	Material, such as brass or copper, which will discolour after a time can be protected by a coating of lacquer.
Tin plating	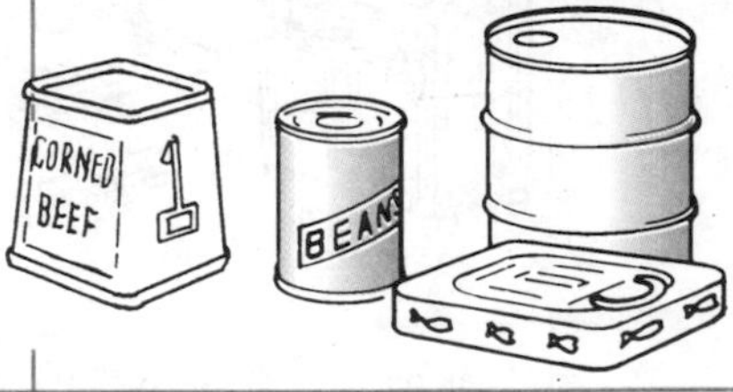	Tin plating protects the surface of steel from corrosion and protects the contents, e.g., food, from contamination by the steel.
Chrome plating		Chrome plating gives a hard, shiny attractive finish. It can be applied to steel or brass.

Fig. 6.25 Finishes

Finish	Uses	Notes
Plastics coating	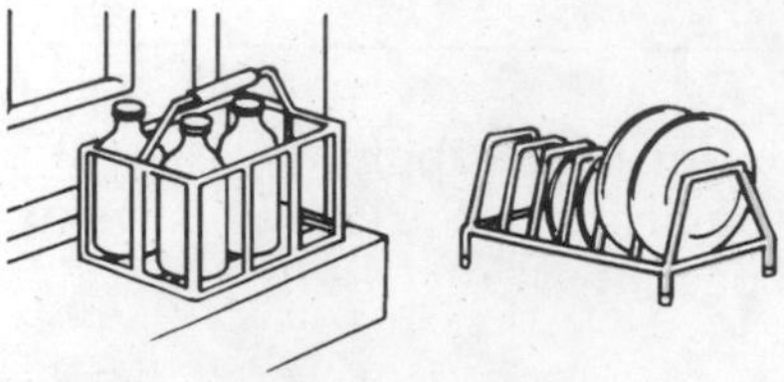	Commonly PVC and polythene are used to 'dip' steel. This is done in a fluidising tank.
Enamelling		Enamels are applied to copper surfaces, which 'fuse' to the surface after heating.
Varnish		Prepare surface thoroughly. Apply two *thin* coats. Rub down between coats. Clean brushes with white spirit.
Primer, undercoat and paint	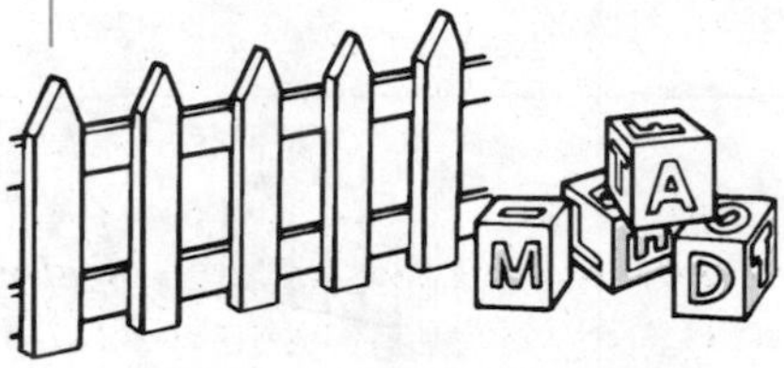	Top coat will only stick properly to an undercoat. The primer is designed to fill the grain of the timber.
Cellulose paint	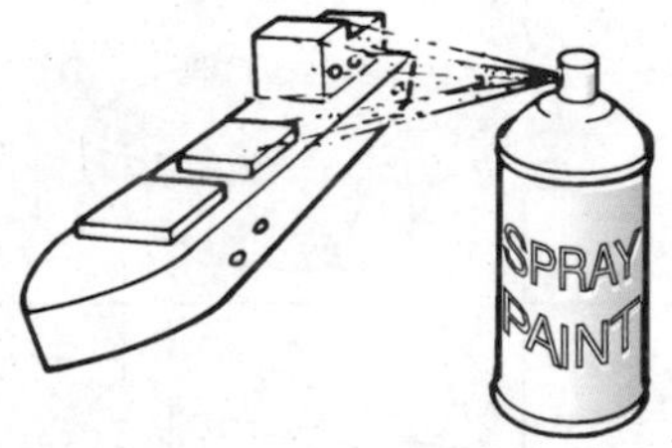 SPRAY PAINT	Aerosols containing CFCs should be avoided. Cellulose vapour is harmful. You must ensure good ventilation and wear a face mask.
French polish	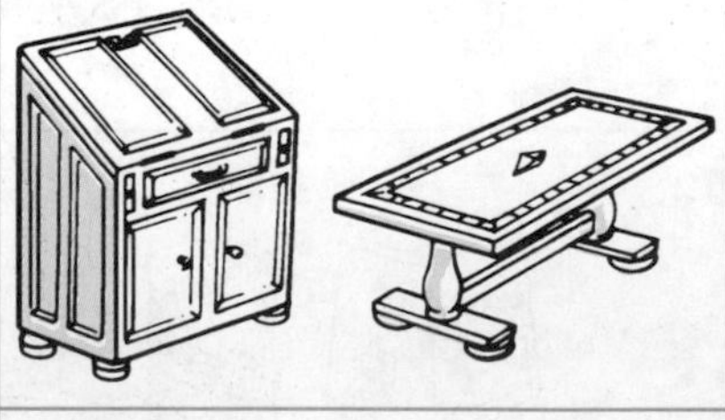	A difficult process best left to the experts. The finished surface is of a high gloss but is easily damaged by heat.
Oil	 Teak oil Linseed oil Olive oil	Oils provide good resistance to water. They are quick and easy to apply.

Fig. 6.25 Finishes (continued)

6.5 Manufacturing processes

It is very important that you are aware of some of the main industrial manufacturing processes in the main resistant materials. When deciding upon the most appropriate manufacturing process, designers need to consider the following:

- how many products are going to be produced and at what rate – the scale of production
- the form of the product (in terms of its shape, intricacy, complexity)
- the material to be used

Understanding how products are made in industry and why particular processes are used is an important part of resistant materials technology.

Plastic moulding

Injection moulding

Injection moulding, as its name suggests, involves injecting molten thermoplastic into a mould under great pressure. The moulds can be very intricate and are often made in several pieces. Radio housings, computer casings, vacuum cleaners and watches are all made by injection moulding. Injection moulding is a widely used process for making products in volume. It would never be used for one-off or small batch production. This is because the tooling cost for the machines is very expensive. However, once set up, the products (or mouldings) can be produced very cheaply. Typically, complex moulds for a product such as vacuum cleaner would cost £50,000–£100,000.

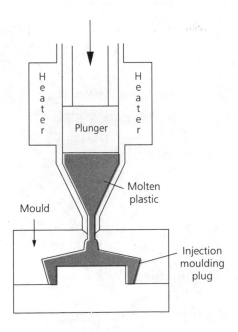

Fig. 6.26 Injection moulding

Extrusion

This process involves forcing a molten thermoplastic through a die and rapidly cooling the resultant shape as it emerges. This is used for making products such as drain pipes/guttering and UPVC window frames.

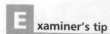

Examiner's tip

Look at a plastic bottle, you will see a seam down both sides where the mould has come together, you will also see a fold of plastic underneath the base where the tube of plastic was gripped.

Blow moulding

Blow moulding, as its name suggests, involves blowing air into a sealed thermoplastic sheet or tube. The process is very similar to glass blowing and is used for the industrial production of bottles and containers. A tube of hot (therefore very flexible) thermoplastic is gripped at both ends by the mould and air is blown into the tube which then takes the shape of the mould.

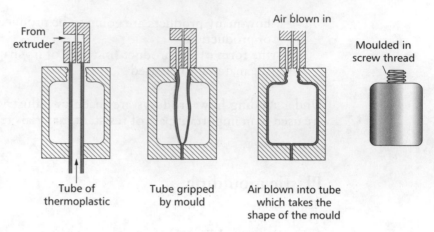

Fig. 6.27 Extrusion blow moulding

Vacuum forming

A common process in schools. A flat sheet of thermoplastic is heated until it becomes very flexible, the air is then sucked out from below the sheet which draws it down over the mould. In industry, vacuum forming is widely used for producing large components such as car dashboards, baths (made from acrylic) and bubble packaging of goods. It is a relatively low-cost form of production and is therefore appropriate for small batch production right through to continuous mass production.

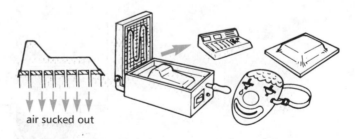

Fig. 6.28 Vacuum forming

All of the above processes are used with **thermoplastics**. The advantage of using thermoplastics is that there is no scrap produced. Any mouldings that are rejected are merely chopped up and reused, something which cannot be done with thermosetting plastics such as urea formaldehyde.

Compression moulding

The most common moulding process for thermosets is compression moulding. This process involves placing a 'plug' of mixed thermoset between two halves of a split mould. The mould closes and under great heat and pressure the moulding is 'cured' for approximately two minutes. During this curing time the cross links are formed in the thermoset, setting the moulding permanently in its shape. This process is widely used in industry for making components such as fan housings, electrical plugs and sockets.

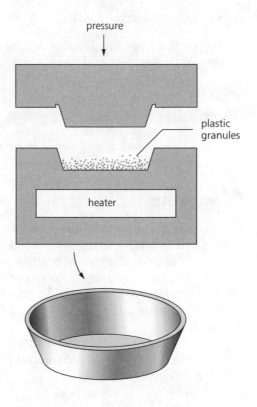

Fig. 6.29 Compression moulding

GRP (fibreglass) moulding

Another widely used process involving the use of thermosets is the production of glass reinforced polyester (GRP or fibreglass). GRP is a composite – a material which is formed from a mixture of materials, which when formed has different properties than the constituent parts. GRP has high tensile and compressive strength, is light, hard wearing and has excellent resistance to corrosion. Some car bodies are made from GRP as are many small boats and vehicles such as milk floats.

Casting in aluminium

There are two main methods used for casting aluminium: **sand casting** and **die casting**. Sand casting involves making a wooden split mould, called a pattern, which is the same shape as the product to be produced. Each half of the pattern is packed with a special sand in steel boxes. When the pattern is removed, a perfect mould is made in the sand. Molten aluminium is then poured into the mould.

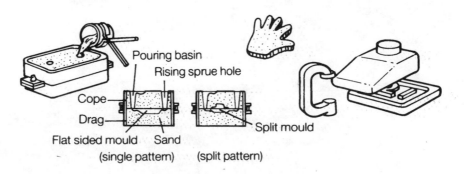

Fig. 6.30 Casting in aluminium

Advantages of sand casting

- it is a low-initial outlay production process
- it is ideally suited to large products which do not require high levels of accuracy

Disadvantages of sand casting

- a new sand mould needs to be made every time
- it is relatively slow

Die casting

Die casting (sometimes called gravity die casting) uses moulds made from high carbon steel. Unlike sand casting moulds these can be used over and over again. The initial cost of the mould is quite high, therefore die casting is only used where higher scales of production are needed. High production rates can be achieved from **pressure die casting**. Pressure die casting involves injecting molten aluminium into a die under great pressure (similar to injection moulding in plastics).

Aluminium is often extruded into long lengths.

Fabrication – adding pieces together

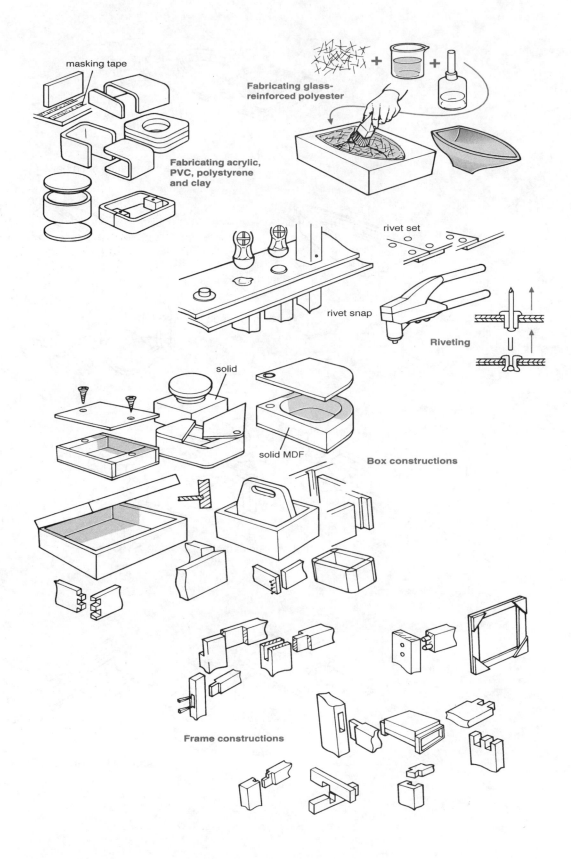

masking tape

Fabricating glass-
reinforced polyester

Fabricating acrylic,
PVC, polystyrene
and clay

rivet set

rivet snap

Riveting

solid

solid MDF

Box constructions

Frame constructions

Fig. 6.31 Fabrication

Deforming

laminating in timber

bending plywood

hot working of metal

straight bend in thermoplastics

Fig. 6.32 Deforming

Wasting – removing parts

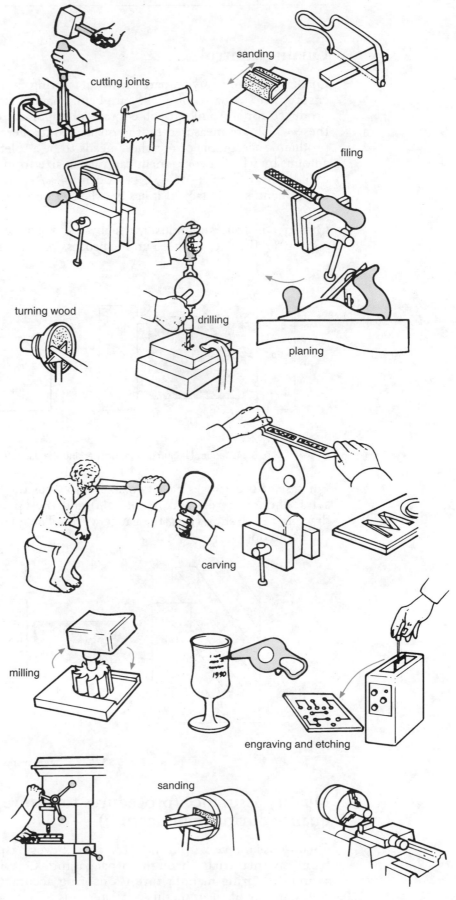

Fig. 6.33 Wasting

6.6 Quality

Quality control

Quality control is a vital part of manufacturing in industry; it involves **testing** to ensure that standards of quality are being maintained. When a working drawing is produced for a product it will contain all important dimensions and sizes and it is these which are measured by the quality controller. In order to decide whether a product is acceptable or not there needs to be a tolerance set. The **tolerance** is the amount by which a component can vary in size from the absolute size. Tolerance is usually stated as + or –, e.g. 100 mm +/–1%. This would mean that the component is acceptable if it lies between 99 mm and 101 mm.

Quality controllers in industry usually test a sample of manufactured components – say 10%. In order to speed up the process they use specially designed gauges.

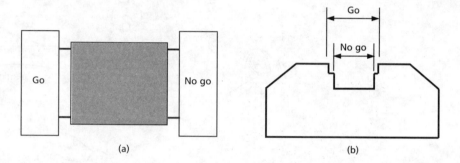

Fig. 6.34 Gauges (a) Plug gauge for checking the diameter of a hole (b)Length gauge

For ease of use, gauges have two sizes known as the 'go' and the 'no go'. These are set at the lower tolerance (size – %) and the upper tolerance (size + %). The drawing below shows how the gauge works. The go end goes into the hole whereas the no go does not.

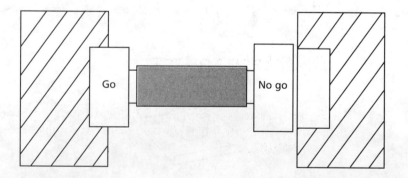

Fig. 6.35 How a gauge works

Quality assurance (procedures to ensure consistency and quality during manufacture)

Quality assurance within industry covers every aspect of product manufacture from raw materials through to packaging. One important aspect of quality assurance during manufacture is ensuring accuracy and consistency. The most common way of ensuring this consistency is to use jigs and fixtures.

Imagine that four holes are to be drilled accurately and consistently on 1000 pieces of steel (see Fig. 6.36). A jig would need to be designed to:

- clamp the work
- guide the cutter (in this case a drill bit)

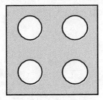

Fig. 6.36

The steel plate is clamped within the jig using the lever-operated cam as shown in Fig. 6.37. Hardened steel bushes guide the drill bits into the correct position. Hardened steel must be used to prevent wear in the bushes which would cause inaccuracies as the jig was used repeatedly.

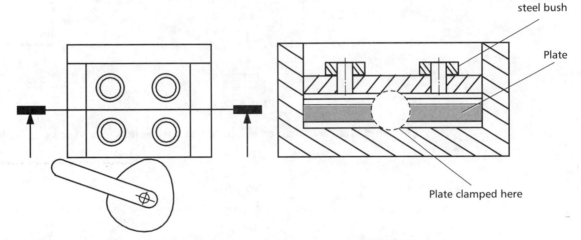

Fig. 6.37 Section through jig showing plate held in place

A fixture differs from a jig in that it is fixed to the bed of the machine tool, whereas a jig is movable in order to line up with the tooling.

6.7 Mechanisms

A mechanism is a device which turns one kind of force into another, for example by turning the handle on a door lock (turning force), the latch moves forwards and backwards.

There are five basic types of mechanism:

Levers: these enable a small amount of force to exert a larger force at a particular point.

Rotary systems: these include pulleys and belts, gears and sprockets which transmit force, and change the direction of speed and movement.

Linkages: these link together different systems and have the important function of changing the direction and size of the force. They can also enable things to move parallel to each other.

Cams and cranks: these convert rotary motion to linear movement.

Screws: these allow a rotary motion to exert a linear (straight line) force, a good example is a G-cramp or vice.

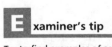

Examiner's tip

Try to find examples of each of these conversions.

Levers

These are simple mechanisms which create 'advantage' to the user. That is, a small force over a large distance enables a much greater force to be exerted over a smaller distance. There are three keys parts to all levers; the effort (the effort put in by the user), the load (the weight or force exerted by the object) and the fulcrum (the point at which the lever pivots).

Fig. 6.38

The type of lever in Fig. 6.38 is called a **first-class** lever.

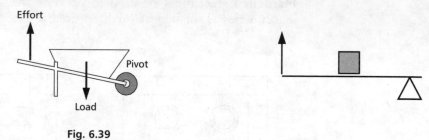

Fig. 6.39

The wheel barrow is an example of a **second-class** lever (see Fig. 6.39).

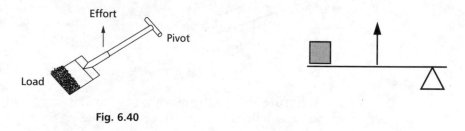

Fig. 6.40

The spade is an example of a **third-class** lever (see Fig. 6.40).

Mechanical advantage

This enables a large force to be exerted with a relatively small effort. Mechanical advantage (MA) is the ratio of the effort put in (input force) divided by the load (output force).

$$MA = \frac{load}{effort}$$

Example

A 20 Newton effort is needed on the handles of a wheelbarrow to lift the 100N load it contains.

$$MA = \frac{Load}{Effort} = \frac{100}{20} = 5$$

Therefore the lever has a MA of 5.

Velocity ratio

This is the distance moved by the effort divided by the distance moved by the load.

$$VR = \frac{\text{distance moved by effort}}{\text{distance moved by load}}$$

Example

The handles of a wheelbarrow are lifted 600 mm whilst the load rises by 100 mm.

$$VR = \frac{600}{100} = 6 \text{ or a ratio of 6:1}$$

Efficiency

Having calculated the mechanical advantage and the velocity ratio it is now possible to calculate the efficiency of a system (theoretically it should be 100%). Friction in actual systems will always reduce its efficiency.

$\text{Efficiency} = \frac{MA}{VR} \times 100\%$ which for the wheel barrow above $= \frac{5}{6} \, 100\% = 83\%$

Mechanical advantage, velocity ratio and the efficiency can be used on any mechanism, they are not limited to levers.

Linkages

These are very useful mechanisms because they allow forces and motion to be transmitted where they are needed. Some common examples are given in Fig. 6.41.

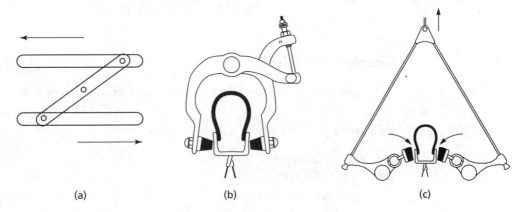

(a)   (b)   (c)

Fig. 6.41 (a) Reverse action linkage (b) The Bell crank mechanism (c) Mountain bike brakes

Parallel motion linkage (opposite sides stay parallel)

This type of linkage is based upon the parallelogram.

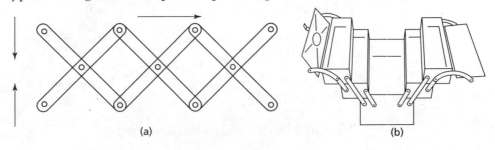

(a)   (b)

Fig.6.42 (a) Parallel motion linkage (b) Cantilever toolbox

Rotary systems

Many products use rotary mechanisms to transmit power. The three main types of rotary mechanisms are:

- gears
- pulleys and belts
- chain and sprockets

Gears

These are used in situations where force needs to be transmitted without slip. Gears are toothed wheels, fixed to the driver and the driven shaft. Two gears in mesh will turn in opposite direction to one another. By using an 'idler' gear, the driver and driven gears can be made to turn in the same direction (Fig. 6.43).

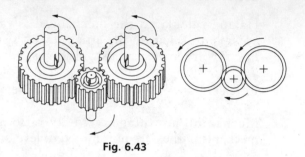

Fig. 6.43

Gear ratios (changing the speed)

$$\text{Gear ratio} = \frac{\text{number of teeth of driven gear}}{\text{number of teeth on driver}}$$

Simple gear trains

A simple gear train is a system which only has one driver and one driven gear.

Example

Driver gear 20 teeth
Driven gear 60 teeth

$$\text{Ratio} = \frac{20}{60} = 2:6 \text{ or } 1:3$$

The driven gear rotates at 1/3 the speed of the driver gear.

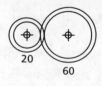

20   60

Fig. 6.44

Example

Driver gear 50 teeth
Driven gear 25 teeth

$$Ratio = \frac{50}{25} = 2:1$$

The driven gear rotates at twice the speed of the driver.

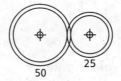

Fig. 6.45

Complex gear trains

With complex gear trains, the driven gear will have another gear attached to the same shaft which will in turn drive another gear. Complex gear trains are needed to achieve large reductions in speed. With reduction gears, as speed decreases (by stepping down the gears) the torque (turning force) of the driven gear increases.

Example

$$Ratio = \frac{driver}{driven}(A) \times \frac{driver}{driven}(B)$$

Driver gear (A) 50 teeth
Driven gear 10 teeth
Driver gear (B) 80 teeth
Driven gear 20 teeth

$$\frac{50}{10} \times \frac{80}{20} \text{ or } 5:1 \times 4:1 = 20:1$$

The driven gear will rotate at 20 times the speed of the driver.

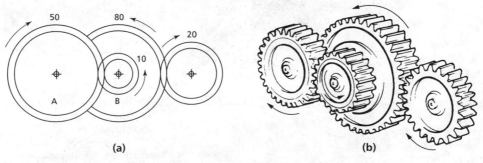

(a)　　　　　　　　　　　(b)

Fig. 6.46

Gears can also be used to change direction. Two special gears are used for this purpose: a pair of **bevel gears** (as in a hand drill) or a **worm and wheel**.

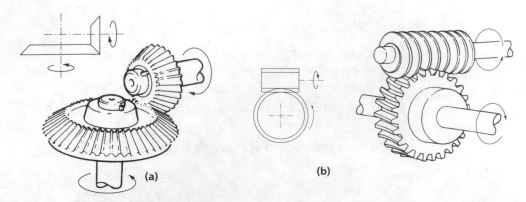

Fig. 6.47 (a) Bevel gears (b) Worm gear and wormwheel

Rack-and-pinion gears

Using a special gear mechanism called a rack-and-pinion, gears can be used to convert rotary to linear motion.

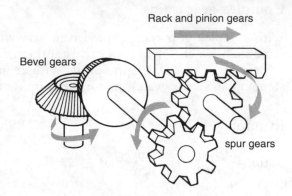

Fig. 6.48 Rack-and-pinion

Fig. 6.49 shows commonly used products which use gears.

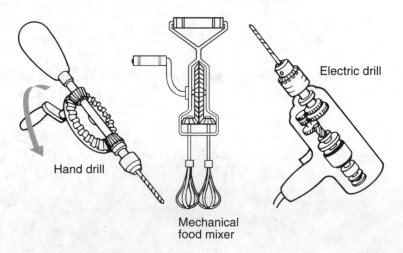

Fig. 6.49 Everyday machines containing gears

Pulleys and belts

Pulleys use vee belts to transmit force. Unlike gears, the driver and driven pulley rotate in the same direction.

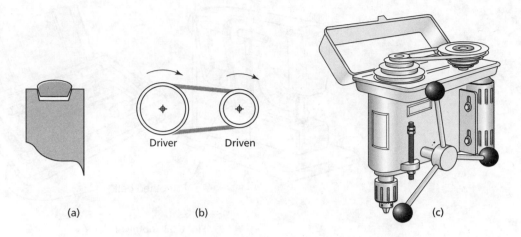

Fig. 6.50 (a) Cross-section of vee belt (b) Pulley (c) Pillar drill

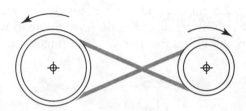

Fig. 6.51

Belt crossed – driver and driven pulley rotate in opposite directions.

Cone pulleys are used on a pillar drill to achieve different speeds.

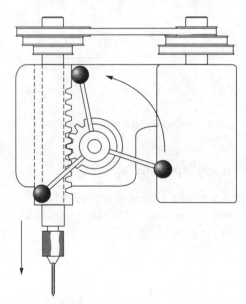

Fig. 6.52

Advantages of pulleys and belts

- belts are quiet, unlike metal gears
- belts do not need to be oiled
- belts can be stretched to get them on
- it is very easy to change the direction of motion by simply crossing the belt

The biggest disadvantage with belts is that they slip. In order to ensure a non-slip drive, toothed belts are often used.

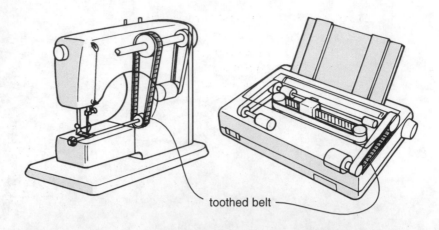

toothed belt

Fig. 6.53 Toothed belts

A single pulley can also be used as a lifting device, but a better system involves using two pulleys as shown. When an effort is applied for 5 metres the load will rise by 2.5 metres. This gives a velocity ratio (VR) of 2. Assuming there is no appreciable friction in the pulleys, the load will be twice the effort. Therefore this system will give a mechanical advantage of 2.

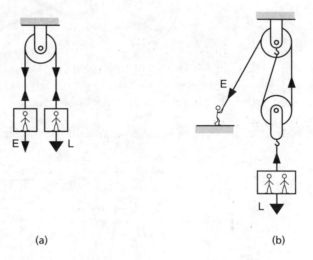

(a)

(b)

Fig. 6.54 (a) Using a pulley as a lifting device (b) Using two pulleys to increase efficiency

Chain and sprockets

A sprocket is a toothed wheel driven by a chain (a series of metal links). Bicycles and motor bikes use sprockets and chains because of their strength and the fact that they do not slip.

Fig. 6.55

Advantages of chain and sprockets:

- larger forces can be transmitted
- chains do not slip
- the links on a chain can be taken apart and removed for maintenance

Cams and cranks

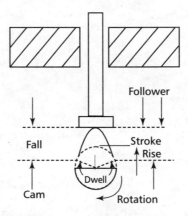

Fig. 6.56

Cams are widely used mechanisms which convert rotary to linear motion. As the cam rotates the follower moves up and down (reciprocating motion). The amount of travel the follower makes is dependent upon the shape of the cam.

Types of cam

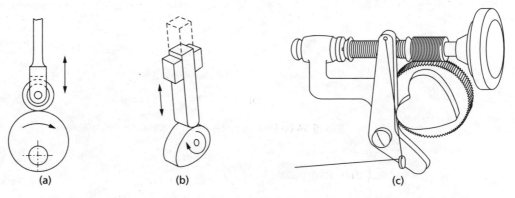

Fig. 6.57 Types of cam (a) Circular cam (b) Pear-shaped cam (c) Heart-shaped cam

Crank and slider

A crank and slider convert rotary motion to linear (reciprocating) motion. Used in car engines (the crank shaft) and on machines such as a power hacksaw.

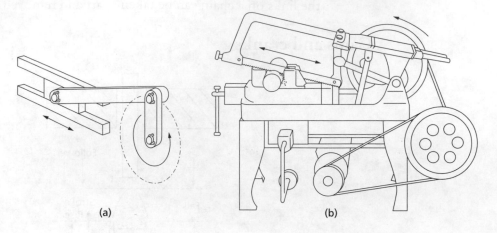

(a)   (b)

Fig. 6.58 (a) Crank and slider mechanism (b) Power hacksaw

The distance travelled by the slider is dependent upon the radius of the crank.

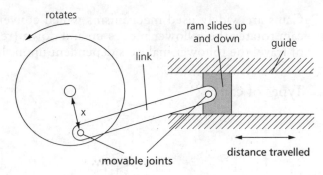

Distance travelled equals twice x

Fig. 6.59

Chapter 7
Textiles technology

7.1 Equipment

You will be expected to be able to select, describe and use the following tools and equipment:

Equipment	Uses	Appearance
Scissors and shears	Shears are used for cutting out the fabric, whilst the smaller scissors are required for trimming and cutting thread.	
Pinking shears	For finishing seams on fabric that will not fray.	
Textile scissors	Used for snipping off thread ends .	
Tailor's chalk	Used for marking out accurately on darker fabrics, prior to cutting.	
Tracing wheel	Used with dressmaker's carbon for transferring markings	
Tape and metre rule	A tape is used for taking measurements, while a rule is used for measuring the fabric itself.	
Paper patterns	Made from thin tissue, they are used as a template to cut fabric to the required shape.	

Equipment	Uses	Appearance
Pins	Used to temporarily hold fabric together or mark positions.	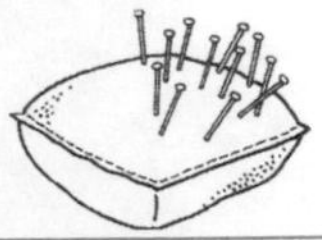
Thimbles	Protects the fingers when hand sewing, especially for long periods or when using tough /thick fabrics	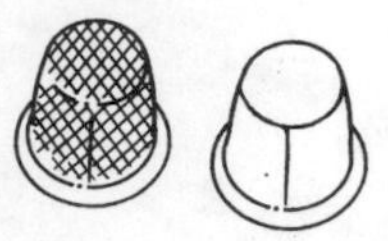
Needles	Used for sewing and embroidery. It is important to select the correct size and type for the task. Types include – betweens, sharps, milliner's or straw, crewel, tapestry and chenille.	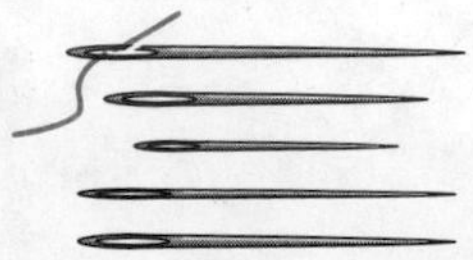
Machine needles	Specially designed for working with sewing machines. Once again the selection of the correct needle for the fabric and thread is important.	
Bodkin	Made from metal or plastic, it is used for threading cord or elastic through hems and casings.	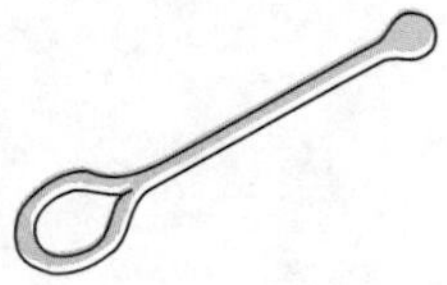
Embroidery frame	Maintains tension in a fabric by enclosing it in two sprung rings.	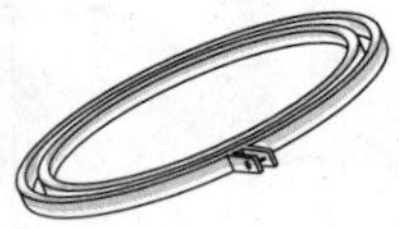
Iron – dry or steam	Used to remove unwanted creases or deliberately form creases. Available in various weights.	
Ironing board	Used to place clothes on when pressing. Should be adjustable for height.	
Sleeve board	Should have a velvet pressing board available as well for use with pile fabrics.	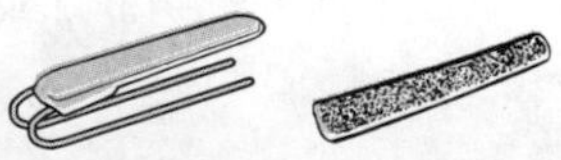
Knitting machine	Can be hand or automatically operated by the use of punchcard or buttons. Many machines are capable of being computer controlled.	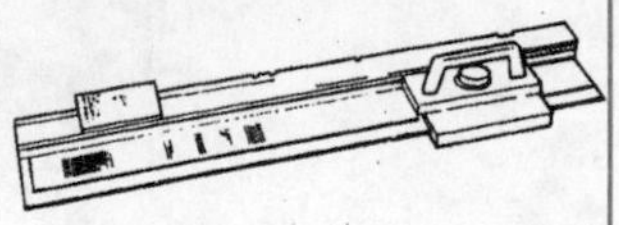
Sewing machine	See Fig. 7.2.	See Fig. 7.2.

Fig.7.1 Textile tools and equipment

7.2 The sewing machine

The sewing machine is the 'workhorse' of textile technology.

Many of today's machines are programmable with more sophisticated ones being computer controlled. A wide range of stitch selections are available and some machines are designed to carry out specialist tasks, e.g. overlocker.

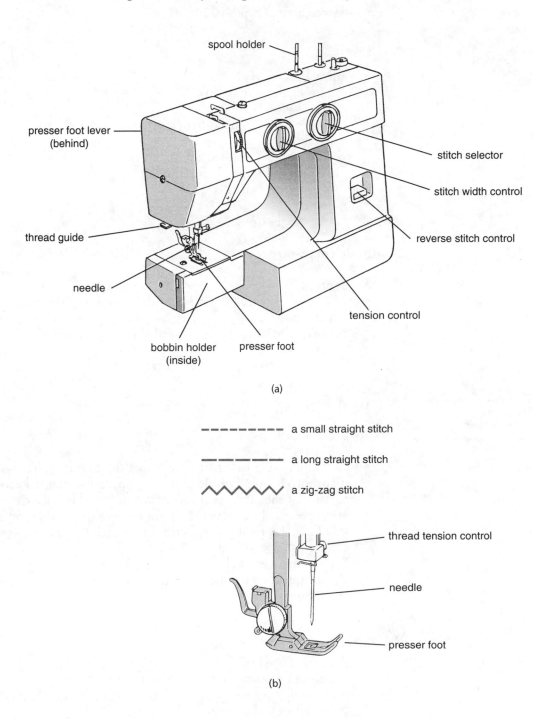

(a)

(b)

Fig. 7.2 (a) Modern sewing machine (b) Details of sewing machine foot

7.3 Fibres and their properties

Textiles uses **fabrics** which are made out of **fibres**. Fibres can be short in length (known as **staple fibres**) requiring spinning into a **yarn** before use, or long (known as **filaments**) which can be used as they are, or chopped and spun into a yarn. Filament fibres can also be processed further to increase their bulk by introducing small loops, curls and twists which produces a thicker, springier yarn.

There are two distinct types of fibres:

Natural

- animal
  - silk – silkworm
  - wool – sheep
  - hair – camel, goat (mohair, cashmere), horse, rabbit (angora)
- vegetable
  - seed – cotton, kapok, coir
  - bast – flax, hemp, jute
  - leaf – manila, sisal
- mineral
  - asbestos

Synthetic (man-made)

- synthetic polymer
  - polyvinyl, polyurethane, polyester, polyamide (nylon)
- natural polymer
- rubber, regenerated protein and cellulose, cellulose
- other
  - carbon, glass fibre, ceramic, metal

Natural fibres

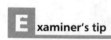

Examiner's tip

You should revise the *origin* of a wide range of fibres

Cotton

- A staple fibre, made from the fibres surrounding the seed head of the plant, producing durable fabrics – especially the thicker varieties. The texture of the fabric is smooth and firm and it is easy to sew.
- It creases badly, but washes and irons well. Suitable for light clothing and bed linen, especially when combined with polyester to reduce the creasing. Poor elasticity.
- Will accept dyes well, but lacks lustre unless treated.
- Burns quickly with the smell of burning paper and remains alight out of the flame.

Wool

- A staple fibre with a natural crimp which produces hard-wearing fabric which can be firm to very soft in texture. Depending on the weave, it is reasonably easy to sew, producing warm clothing. Suitable for soft furnishings and carpets.
- It absorbs water but shrinks badly, requiring damp-pressing. However, it is naturally elastic and will press back into shape well. Will shed creases well, while holding pressed creases.
- Will accept dyes very well.
- It will smoulder in a flame, with the smell of burning hair, but extinguishes itself out of the flame.

Linen

- A staple fibre, made from the stem of the flax plant, that is strong and hard wearing, easy to sew and good for producing thick fabrics that have a firm to rough texture. Increasingly expensive to produce but suitable for tea towels, table cloths and napkins.
- It absorbs water well, but creases easily and therefore needs ironing, which gives it a good lustre.
- Will accept dyes very well.
- Burns in a similar manner to cotton, but with a flame that flares.

Silk

- A filament fibre, produced by unravelling the cocoon of the silkworm in water. This very fine filament can be used as it is, but can also be chopped and spun or processed to increase its bulk by adding loops and twists to give a thicker and more elastic yarn.
- It can produce a strong, hard-wearing fabric which is smooth to soft in texture, with an excellent sheen. The finer weaves need careful handling and although it is reasonably crease resistant and good in water, it needs ironing.
- Will accept dyes well.
- Burns slowly with a yellow flame, with a smell like burning hair, but going out when not in the flame.

Synthetic fibres

Polyester

- A filament or staple fibre, made from ethylene glycol and terephthalic acid. It has poor elasticity, but the spun fibres can be crimped to improve this (crimplene).
- As it washes well, drips dry and resists creasing, it is often mixed with cotton for shirts and blouses. It can also be woven into a heavier fabric for suits and it holds a pressed crease very well, although tends to build up static.
- Does not dye well at home.
- Burns with a sooty flame, melting and shrinking, and self extinguishes.

Acrylic

- A filament fibre made from oil, but more often used as a staple fibre knitted yarn form to produce an inexpensive wool 'substitute', that wears well, but is not as warm when used on its own and builds up static.
- It does not absorb water and therefore is poor for dyeing, but drips dry.
- Burns quickly with a spluttering flame and an acrid smell. It also remains alight out of the flame.

Polyamide (nylon)

- Produced as a filament and staple fibre from chemicals derived from oil and coal. A smooth, cold fibre but with much improved thermal properties in its 'brushed' form.
- Strong and hard wearing, it washes and dries very well, being extremely crease resistant,
- Fairly difficult to sew, it is generally used for shirts, tights, stockings, carpets and waterproof clothing but builds up static readily.
- It takes a dye reasonably well.
- It melts rather than burns, but droplets carry a blue/yellow flame.

Polypropylene

- Another filament fibre synthesised from chemicals which produces a very strong and hard-wearing yarn that is used for ropes, carpets and furnishings. It is non-absorbent and is fairly slippery.
- Burns with a yellow/blue flame and little smoke, producing burning droplets that go out and smell of candle wax.

Viscose

- A filament and staple fibre, made from cellulose obtained from wood pulp. It is spun wet, producing an inexpensive, shiny, not particularly durable fabric that is used for linings.
- Care needs to be taken with sewing and washing, as seams may pull.
- Burns continuously with a yellow flame.

Acetate

xaminer's tip

You should revise carefully the common properties and uses of three natural and three synthetic fibres, and the advantages of two fibre combinations - including polyester/cotton.

- A filament and staple fibre, made from wood pulp. It is spun dry to produce a smooth, slippery and shiny fabric that is used for linings of suits and skirts.
- Care needed when sewing, but is fairly durable.
- Burns easily with a yellow flame, cracking and shrivelling, giving off the smell of vinegar.

Elastene (Lycra)

- A filament fibre, that is smooth and strong, with a good elasticity which makes it a less perishable substitute for rubber.
- Very poor absorbency makes it good for drying and it is used in swimwear, underwear and interlinings.
- Does not take a dye well.

7.4 Yarns

Yarns are made by spinning fibres and filaments. The properties of the fabric will depend on the yarn used.

Carding

Staple fibres, such as wool, need to be separated as they are too matted to be used as they are. This is done by passing two wire brushes (carders) across the fibres in opposite directions to pull the fibres apart.

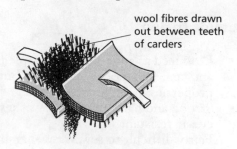

wool fibres drawn out between teeth of carders

Fig. 7.2 Carding by hand

This can also be done on an industrial scale by machine carding, using the same principle.

Spinning

Although some filament fibres are suitable for use in the form they are produced, most fibres are then spun into yarns. It is the type of spinning that changes further the properties of the yarn and ultimately the fabric produced.

Bulky yarns required for knitting have a long twist, but thinner fabrics require a yarn with more twist to increase its strength.

7.5 Fabrics

Fabric is constructed in a number of ways.

Weaving

A loom is used to hold lengths of yarn in position. These longitudinal threads are called the **warp**.

Another yarn (or yarns), known as the **weft**, is then interwoven across the warp and pressed home.

The loom can be used to control the tension of the threads and the density of the finished fabric.

Different patterns and texture can be introduced by changing the colours of the warp and weft and also by adjusting the number and location of the warp threads missed out by the interweaving of the weft thread.

The range of effects produced by the latter have names such as twill, hopsack and satin.

Because the weft threads have been woven, the fabric produced will tend to stretch very slightly more across the weft than it does along the warp. It stretches the most at an angle across the warp and weft.

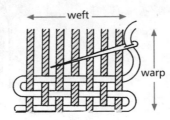

Fig. 7.3 Weaving – showing warp and weft threads.

Knitting

Knitting by hand is a slow process, but is considered a satisfying pastime and allows extremely creative effects to be produced. However, the process can be readily mechanised for commercial purposes.

The yarn is formed into loops which are then interlocked to form the fabric. Texture and pattern changes can made by altering the thickness and type of yarn, the size of the needles (and therefore the size of loops formed) and the combination of the basic stitches used – plain and purl.

Knitted fabrics stretch in all directions, but return to shape as long as they haven't been overstretched or stretched in the same way on a regular basis.

The air-pockets created by the knitting process enhance the thermal properties of the yarn used.

Fig. 7.4 Knitting

Crocheting

A hand technique used for producing intricate and decorative fabrics and edgings. The yarn is looped with the use of a crotchet hook, with the chains produced being interlinked to produce the patterned fabrics. The general effect is one of a fabric with 'holes'.

Fig. 7.5 Crocheting

Macramé

Another hand technique producing a product with holes. Much thicker yarns, such as plaited yarns and strips of material, string, cord and ropes, tend to be used than in crochet which are then knotted together to produce strong fabrics that can be used as hammocks, hangers, rugs and wallhangings. The main knots employed are the square knot and the clove hitch.

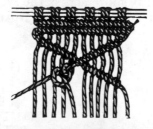

Fig. 7.6 Macramé

Felting and bonding

Cheap and quick to make, the fibres are formed into the fabric by a combination of heat, moisture and pressure. Felts are useful for carpet underlays that require little inherent strength or wearing properties. They are also used for hats because the fabric can be shaped without seams by the further application of heat, moisture and pressure. An example of a bonded fabric is the disposable cloth.

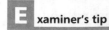

Examiner's tip

You should, by disassembly, investigate thoroughly the construction of two woven and knitted fabrics and one felted or bonded fabric.

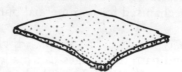

Fig. 7.7 Felting

See Unit 2.11, Fig. 2.17 for coursework examples using some of these techniques.

7.6 Working properties

Physical properties

A fabric is selected for a particular application based on a number of physical properties:

- washability – its need to be hand washed, machine washed or dry cleaned and its resistance to shrinking when wet
- thermal insulation – its ability to retain or lose heat
- stain resistance – the ease with which spills and marks can be removed
- wear – its resistance to abrasion and tearing in normal use
- elasticity – its capacity to stretch and return to its original shape under working conditions
- absorbency – how well it absorbs and retains liquids
- water resistance – how well it prevents the flow of water
- wind resistance – how well it prevents the passage of air
- fire resistance – its combustibility and the toxicity of fumes given off
- machinability – the ease with which it can be sewn and made up

A number of other factors will also affect the choice of fabric:

- cost and availability
- colour range
- weight

Applied surface finishes

The working properties of fabrics can be improved by the application of chemicals to enhance performance. These finishes may have their effectiveness reduced if the fabric is incorrectly treated in aftercare.

Some of the surface treatments include:
- anti-static – to reduce the build-up of static electricity by retaining the moisture which conducts it
- moth proofing – applied mainly to carpets, upholstery and soft furnishings, making the fibres taste unpleasant
- shower and water proofing – helps the water run off the fabric rather than be absorbed
- stain and soil resistance – a mixture of silicone and fluorine applied to carpets and upholstery
- stiffening (trubenising)

7.7 Colouring fabrics

Most fibres, synthetic or natural, do not come in a range of colours. Indeed, natural fibres will often be **bleached** to improve their whiteness.

Dyes

Some synthetic yarns can have a colour pigment added at the manufacturing stage but the remaining yarns will need to be dyed. The fabric can also be dyed after construction.

A dye is said to be **colour fast** if it does not fade during washing. Exposure to sunlight is another common cause of colours fading.

Natural dyes are made from plants, animals and minerals but can be less fast and resistant to fading than synthetic dyes which are chemically produced in a wide range of colours.

Different fibres react in different ways to different dyes, with natural fibres being the best since they are generally more absorbent. Synthetic materials will not readily accept dyes and require chemicals called **mordants** to fix the dyes.

Examiner's tip

You should research and apply tests for dyes in terms of colour fastness and light fastness.

Dyeing fabrics

The basic principle of dyeing is to immerse the fabric in the dye – often after wetting it first to aid even pentration of the dye, rinsing and drying.

When dyeing bought fabrics it is often advisable to thoroughly wash the materials to remove any surface treatments that may have been applied that could effect the quality of the result.

There are a number of methods of dyeing that can be carried out on a small scale which give very effective results, basically relying on controlling where the dye comes in contact with the fabric.

Batik

Hot wax is applied to the fabric – either by a paintbrush, or more traditionally by a tjanting tool – so that it saturates areas that you do *not* want to colour. When the wax is dry, it will *resist* the dye when immersed and only the unwaxed areas will be dyed. A random, 'crazed effect' can be achieved if the fabric is crushed first, as the wax will crack and allow some penetration of the dye. Once the dye has dried, the wax is removed by hot ironing between absorbent sheets of paper. The fact that the wax will melt when heated indicates that only cold water dyes are suitable for this process.

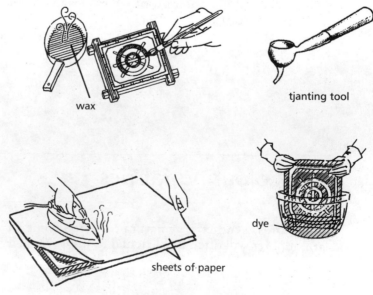

wax

tjanting tool

sheets of paper

dye

Fig. 7.8 Batik dyeing

Tie dyeing

This method relies on tying string, cord or rubber bands, etc. tightly round bundles of the fabric which then resist the dye in random, but in interesting and effective ways. This can be redone a number of times or with small pebbles included in knots of the fabric.

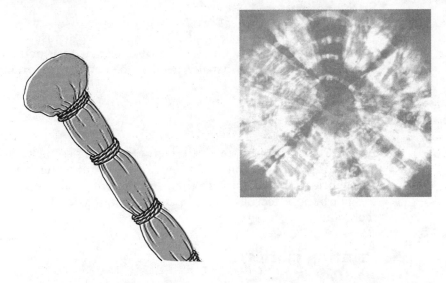

Fig 7.9 Tie dyeing

Tritik

Similar to tie dyeing in that the material is pleated and sewn in order that the dye is resisted in some areas.

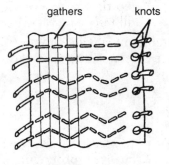

Fig. 7.10 Tritik dyeing

See Unit 2.11, Fig. 2.17 for examples of some of these techniques.

Painting fabrics

Fabric pens and crayons

These are waterproof and available in a wide range of colours. This is an extremely quick and easy way of applying coloured decoration and is ideally suited for one-off items and mock-ups. Transfer crayons are also available, the design being transferred from paper to the fabric by using a hot iron.

Brush painting

The simplest way of applying fabric paints is by a small, soft brush. As the paint needs to be thinned, it is most suitable for light-coloured, thin materials such as silk. In this way, quite detailed decoration can be applied.

Spray painting

Fabric paints can also be applied using a spray diffuser or an air-brush. The best results are obtained with the use of a stencil to block off the areas not to be sprayed. Fabric paints usually need to be set by hot ironing through a sheet of paper.

Marbling

An interesting and impressive effect, resembling colourful marble, can be achieved by floating the paint on the surface of a bath of water containing wallpaper paste. The fabric is pulled through the paint after it has been randomly stirred to create the marbling effect. Oil based paints, as well as fabric paints, are suitable for this technique.

Printing fabrics

For producing repeat patterns, printing methods need to be used.

Block printing

The desired pattern is formed as a relief on the surface of a flat block of wood or lino. Blocks can also be made by attaching shapes from a number of suitable materials – card, rubber, foam, string, etc. Blocks can even be made from vegetables such as potatoes or large carrots. The surface of the block then has the paint applied by a roller and the block is pressed onto the fabric which has been washed and pressed flat. The block is repainted and the process repeated to cover the required area.

Different colours may be subsequently applied on different blocks to create more intricate patterns, but this requires careful **indexing** to avoid unwanted overlapping.

Screen printing

A nylon or polyester fabric is stretched over a frame through which paint can be pushed by a squeegee, producing a very even application of paint with accurate positioning. The fabric to be printed is placed on a flat surface and a stencil made from card or thin plastic is put in position. The screen is then placed onto this and the paint applied.

A more effective method of screen printing is when the mesh is treated with a resist medium to make the stencil unnecessary. This can be done photographically.

Roller printing

Commercially, if large runs of fabric are to be printed, the relief patterns will be put onto rollers which are inked as the fabric is continuously run under them. Checks must be made regularly to ensure that the different coloured elements of the pattern are indexed properly.

This can be achieved on a small scale by the use of a hand roller with the pattern attached.

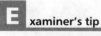

Examiner's tip

Experimentation is extremely worthwhile when trying to achieve a desired effect. Remember, the results should be fully analysed, evaluated and reported in your coursework folio.

7.8 Decoration

The use of coloured fabrics and yarns is not the only means of improving the aesthetic qualities of textile products.

Quilting

A layer of polyester wadding is placed between two layers of fabric and sewn together. The sewing can be at the edge, across in a regular pattern – a diamond for example – or to produce a more creative effect. The resulting 'bulging' is not only decorative, but has the advantage that as air is trapped in the layers of wadding, the thermal insulation properties are markedly improved.

Appliqué

This is simply the sewing onto one fabric, shapes cut from other fabrics to create decoration and illustration. To improve the relief effect, wadding is sometimes included.

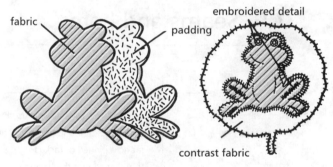

Fig. 7.11 Appliqué

Patchwork

This is the creation of one fabric by sewing together scraps of other fabrics using shapes that **tessellate** – traditionally a hexagon was used. The pieces of fabric are cut out using a **template**, including a seam allowance. These pieces are then systematically and accurately sewn together, allowing for any design that is required to be incorporated within the shapes.

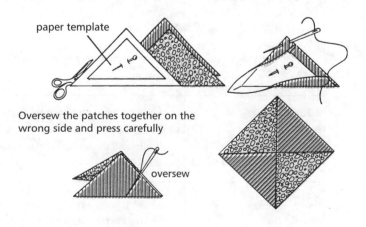

Fig. 7.12 Patchwork decoration

Embroidery

Decorative effects are achieved by coloured threads and yarns being sewn onto the fabric using a wide variety of stitches in combination. Many sewing machines can carry some of the simpler embroidery stitches. Commercially, logos, badges, and motifs are done by programmed machines.

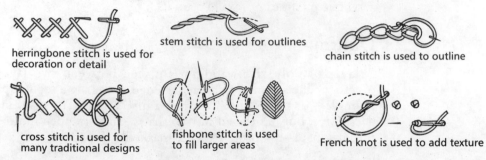

herringbone stitch is used for decoration or detail

stem stitch is used for outlines

chain stitch is used to outline

cross stitch is used for many traditional designs

fishbone stitch is used to fill larger areas

French knot is used to add texture

Fig. 7.13 Examples of embroidery stitches

See Unit 2.11 for coursework examples of some of these techniques

7.9 Seams and hems

Name	Use	Appearance
Plain seam	A simple row of stitches is used to join two pieces of fabric together. The fabric is pinned or tacked right sides together so that the 'spare' material can be pressed flat on the unseen side.	
French seam	A double seam used for fabrics that fray easily. The fabric is stitched with the wrong sides together, but the cut edges are protected.	fold over
Double-stitched seam	A more decorative form of double seam.	
Top-stitched seam	A plain seam with extra stitching for strength.	
Fusible web	A glue impregnated web that is activated by heat is ironed inside the folded hem of skirts and trousers to avoid the use of visible stitches.	web apply hot iron
Slip hemming	Hemming using very small stitches on the inside which are effectively invisible.	tiny stitch

7.14 Types of seams and hems

7.10 Fastenings

Buttons and buttonholes

Capable of being carried out by machine as well as by hand. The buttons are produced in a vast range of shapes and styles and therefore can be considered to be another form of applied decoration.

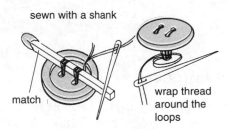

Fig. 7.15 Sewing buttons

Press studs

A simple and easy fastening for situations that are put under little strain. Although they are available in coloured forms, they are not usually used where they will be visible. They are extremely difficult to attach by machine and are generally hand sewn.

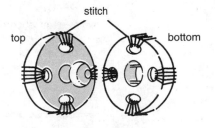

Fig. 7.16 Sewing press

Hooks and eyes

Similar to press studs. The hook and bar is a strong version which can be used on the waistbands of skirts and trousers in place of buttons.

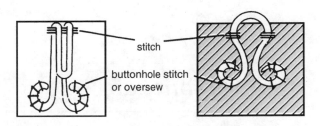

Fig. 7.17 Sewing hooks and eyes

Velcro

A two-part tape used to close openings which will not be under great strain, but require easy access. The effectiveness of the tape is severely reduced if the 'hook' part is contaminated with fluff and other fibres.

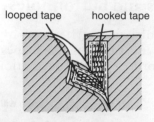

Fig. 7.18 Velcro tape

Zip fasteners

Zips are the most useful form of mechanical fastening in use where the length of the opening needs to be closed and is likely to be put under strain. Even so, it is usually used in conjunction with another form of fastener, especially on trousers and skirts, to act as a back-up and to protect the top teeth of the zip. They can be fitted so that they are visible or hidden, with closed or open ends. They may also be fitted with two-way openers on outer garments, allowing easier access to inner layers.

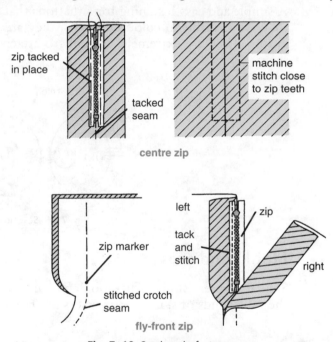

Fig. 7.19 Sewing zip fasteners

7.11 Fabric care

Washing

Fabrics are washed to remove soiling and to help restore them to their original condition. Water, hot or cold, cannot do this efficiently so soap or detergent is added and the fabric agitated in some way – by hand or by machine.

Soaps: mainly made from vegetable oils and caustic soda. They can be coloured and perfumed.

Detergent: made synthetically, they contain molecules that bond with the dirt particles which are then removed by the agitation of the washing machines. Biological powders contain enzymes that help digest the stains. Other additives in detergents enhance the brightness of the fabrics after washing.

The temperature, length and type of wash cycle and drying methods can all affect how well a fabric will wash. It is therefore important to take note of the fabric care label and refer to the instructions on the detergent packet and washing machine controls.

Care should be taken when using some detergents as they can cause allergic reactions in some people.

Ironing and pressing

Ironing: removes the creases that washing and drying puts in some fabrics. The temperature that the iron is set at is critical and so the instructions on the iron and the fabric care label must be adhered to.

Pressing: deliberately forms creases in a fabric such as the creases in trousers or the pleats in a skirt.

Fabric care labels

Most fabric products will have a care label attached which will indicate what the fabric is made from and instructions for its aftercare, usually in the form of symbols (see Fig. 7.20).

Symbol	Instructions
[60]	Machine code – this code, with a number in degrees inside, will indicate precisely the temperature of both machine and hand washing and the type of cycle to be used
(hand wash)	Hand wash only
(crossed wash)	Do not machine or hand wash
Ⓟ	May be dry cleaned – other markings will indicate the process to be used
⊗	Not suitable for dry cleaning
△CL	Bleach – (chlorine bleach) may be used
⨺	Do not bleach
◯	May be tumble dried

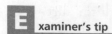
Symbol	Instructions
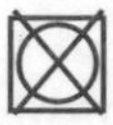	Do not tumble dry
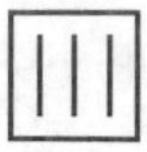	Drip dry
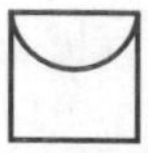	Hang dry
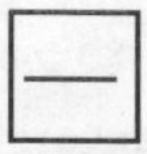	Dry flat
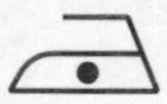	Cool iron
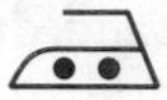	Warm iron
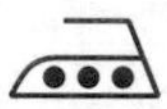	Hot iron
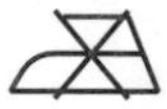	Do not iron

Fig. 7. 20 Fabric care labels

7.12 Computers in textile technology

Data handling

Computer spreadsheets are used to analyse and present information from product development tests, market research and questionnaires, costings, etc.

Product development

Computer graphic programmes can be used to develop designs which can then be analysed to evaluate their production possibilities.

Computer-aided manufacture

Weaving, sewing and knitting machines can be programmed with the designs that have been developed from graphic packages and automatically reproduce patterns in the fabric.

Computer control in manufacture

Automated production systems such as weaving and fabric printing will be computer controlled in such areas as stock control and ordering, quality control, packaging and despatch.

Critical control points will have been highlighted in terms of maintaining product specification and these are monitored continuously and **feedback** given to enable corrective action to be taken.

This is a **closed loop** sytem of **quality control,** the efficiency of which can be critical to profitability, especially if the end product is expensive or the fault goes uncorrected for too long - see Unit 1.4 for further information on systems and control.

Chapter 8

Terminal examination

8.1 Preparing for the examination

Revision plan

Once all your assessed coursework is finished, your teachers will either be completing areas of the syllabus not covered at this stage or, more usually, revising the work already covered in order to prepare you for the terminal examination.

Do not rely on this alone, you could have specific needs that your teacher may not cover when preparing work for the group as a whole.

Prepare a revision plan, taking into account the following points:

- start revising as early as possible and especially once time-consuming elements like coursework have finished. This will give you the chance to find any gaps in your knowledge and to ask the necessary questions before it is too late

- actually write down the plan on paper, noting all the critical dates and times on it, e.g.:

  - examination dates
  - remaining coursework deadlines
  - study leave
  - family occasions such as birthdays, holidays, etc.
  - personal events such as sporting fixtures, days out, etc.

- allow some time for relaxation and exercise, you need to be 'fit' for examinations!

- divide the rest of the time between all your subjects. When allocating amounts of time to each subject, take into account such factors as:

- how well you did in the mock examinations
- how easy you generally find the subject
- how important you consider the subject is with respect to your future plans

- work back from the examinations, taking into account the order that they are to be taken

- use colour-coded blocks to give you a clearer idea of how much time you have allocated to each subject

- take account of how you revise and do not allocate yourself amounts of time that you will not use profitably. Variety in terms of 'little and often', or 'topic by topic' may be a more effective method

- don't be afraid to alter your plan as circumstances change, but try to stick to it as closely as possible!

Revision methods

The purpose of revision should be to :

- reinforce the learning that has already happened
- establish what gaps there are and to fill these gaps
- improve your ability to use this knowledge and understanding in answering questions under examination conditions

Revision requires your notes, textbooks, other aids such as this revision guide, time, application and practice questions.

The effectiveness of your revision could be increased by taking account the following:

- do not just read your notes or a textbook. It is much more effective if you highlight key points as you go, using indexing tabs to locate important aspects and creating 'crib cards' for later, quicker run throughs

- sometimes work with a friend or willing relative. They can test you as you go and prompt you where necessary

- practise questions under strict time conditions, many examinations can turn into 'time trials' if you are not used to working at the required speed. Past papers are extremely useful for this, especially if you can get someone to check them for you. This can then be the basis for further revision

- revise in comfortable but suitable surroundings. Whereas music may help, a television is more likely to distract

- be organised and tidy. Time wasted searching for material in a pile on the floor or on your desk can never be recovered

- practise examination skills as well. Some exams will last over two hours, so you must be able to think and, more importantly, write neatly for that long. This will also be true of a practical examination such as Graphic Products, where you must plan to keep your drawing skills polished

8.2 Types of question

Multiple-choice questions

These are used very rarely, but may appear in some Foundation papers. The method is to discount those you know to be incorrect and think carefully about the remainder.

Other forms of this type of question are 'odd one out' and 'rank order'. Once again, think carefully having read what you have been asked to do and do not rush into ticking the first plausible answer given.

Short-answer questions

A commonly used form of question, especially in Foundation papers. The marks available and the space provided – usually on a pre-printed solid or dotted line – will give you an idea of the amount of information intended to be included in the answer.

Where possible use sentences but if only a brief description is required, be as specific as you can, e.g. coping saw, not just saw.

Structured-answer questions

These will usually start with a stem – a statement which provides the context for the rest of the question – which will be in a number of parts. This is the most common form of question used.

The subject of the stem may be new to you, unless it has been included in pre-examination preparation material sent out by the Board. It will have been chosen because it will allow you to demonstrate your understanding and knowledge by reference to a similar context with which you are more familiar.

The parts of the question are often intended to get harder as they progress and will develop information given in previous parts. It is important that you keep the context of the stem in mind at all times.

Open-ended questions

This type of question is rarely used and is likely to appear only in some Higher papers. It requires an extended answer which you have to develop yourself. It is important to plan your answer in order to ensure that you include all the relevant points you wish to make.

8.3 Key words used in questions

Annotate: The addition of explanatory notes to enhance a drawing or sketch. These notes must be more than just labels.

Choose/Select: This usually involves you selecting a given number of items from a list provided, or from a list that you generated in an earlier part of the question, and commenting further in some way.

For example, **choose TWO** of the features you have listed in the specification and **explain** why they are important.

Comment: Requires a brief analysis of a given situation. It is often useful to back up any statements with examples. In some instances, full sentences may not be necessary.

Compare/Contrast: Requires a discussion of *both* sides of an argument. Although it is likely that you will have to come down in favour on one side, the marks will be given for your knowledge of both sides and the clarity of your argument for the decision you have made.

Describe: You are required to give an account in words, using sentences. Make sure your answer is not just a list, marks will be awarded for the quality of the description as well as the content.

Discuss: Requires an essay type response where you will need to structure the answer carefully and come to a conclusion. You may need to **compare**, **justify** and **evaluate** in this type of question.

Draw/Sketch: Unless in a graphic products examination where these have more specific meanings (see Chapter 5), you are required to provide a visual, non-verbal response to the question. You are not marked on your 'drawing ability', but your sketch must clearly illustrate the points asked for. You must be careful to respond appropriately if the question includes **labelled** or **annotated**.

Evaluate: You are required to make a judgement from an extended analysis in this type of question. The criteria on which to base this judgement may have already be generated in earlier parts of the question. If not, you should include the reasons for the conclusions you have come to.

Explain: You need to demonstrate an understanding of the point in question. It will not be enough just to describe it.

Explore: This is to encourage you to use a variety of approaches – especially in design-based questions.

For example, 'Explore a range of ideas for ...'.

Give: Effectively the same as **name** and **suggest**. You can state your answer.

Identify: This is more than a list or a selection. You should produce a structured response using complete sentences.

Justify: This requires a well argued reason why a 'selection' or 'judgement' has been made. Marks are awarded for the quality of the reasoning as well as the content.

Label: One or two words added to drawings and sketches for further clarity.

List: You are required to simply make a list. If no number is given for the number of items to be included, make it as comprehensive as possible taking note of the amount of space or number of lines given for the answer.

Name: Similar to **list**, but often requires a fuller answer.

Outline: This will be used to show your knowledge of a complex issue in a broad way. It will require a less detailed response than for **describe**.

Produce: This is an instruction for you to do something. It will generally involve you 'drawing' or 'writing' after analysing some given information.

Suggest: Similar to **name**, but often linked to a specific context.

Using: This is an instruction to clarify the way in which you should respond to a question.

For example 'Using **sketches**, show how...'. Marks will be lost if this instruction is not followed.

Write: Indicates to you that a written response is required and that sketches, tables, etc. will gain marks only if they improve the quality of the written aspects of the answer.

For example, 'Write a plan for the production of...'.

8.4 Examination do's and don'ts

Do

- get a good night's sleep.

- have your normal meals.

- read the instruction rubric well. It contains important information such as the length of the paper, number of questions to be answered, existence of information sheets, etc.

- read the whole paper before you select your questions (if you have a choice), making sure that you attempt to answer those which should allow you to gain the most marks possible.

- make sure you read each question very carefully and answer only what you have been asked. Be aware that **highlighted words in bold type** are a further reminder of what is required from the answer and what type of answer is required – see Unit 8.3.

- look for clues given by the Examiner. Sometimes answers are given in the text of questions, or can be found in other parts of the paper.

- allocate time to each question in proportion to the marks available. Remember, this will be indicated in brackets, e.g. (5 marks), at the end of each part of a question. Be strict with yourself – it is pointless to lose the chance of answering a ten-mark question by spending too much time on a five-mark question!

- plan to leave yourself time to re-read each response.

- take medicines, inhalers, handkerchiefs, etc. into the examination if you require them and make sure that the examination officer is aware of any medical conditions.

- raise your hand if you have any problems, even though some questions are not allowed to be answered by the invigilators.

- KEEP CALM! Use the time available to your best advantage.

Don't

- stay up all night cramming

- arrive at the examination room late

- forget the equipment that you need. It is advisable to have spare pens and pencils.

- rush your answers. An illegible answer cannot gain any marks. Neither can a correct answer to a question that hasn't been set!

- be fooled into choosing to attempt a question by an apparently easy start. Remember that the early parts to a long question are often easier than the later parts which also carry more marks.

- be tempted to cheat in any way. This can jeopardise all your results.

- GIVE UP OR PANIC!

8.5 Specimen questions

The questions that follow have either been labelled :

- (F)   Foundation tier only

- (F/H)   Foundation and Higher tier

- (H)   Higher tier only

As a rule of thumb, you should allow yourself **one minute per mark** when attempting these questions once you have read them. The mark schemes indicate what should have been included in the answer and how the marks are distributed.

Electronic products

1 (F) The system shown below automatically turns on a porch light when it gets dark.

(a) From the list below, underline **one** suitable input sensor for this sytem   (2 marks)

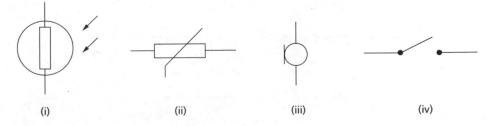

(b) Name each of the circuit symbols shown above.   (4 marks)

A circuit diagram for the system is given below.

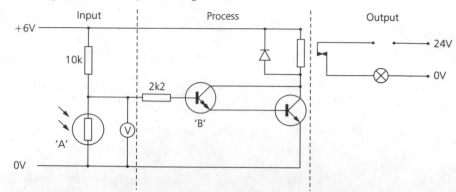

(c) Name component 'B' (2 marks)

(d) Explain the purpose of component 'B' (2 marks)

The input sensor uses a potential divider.

(e) Explain what is meant by the term potential divider. (2 marks)

The resistance of component 'A' varies according to the amount of light falling upon it.

(f) What will be the resistance of component 'A' when the voltmeter (V) reads :

      (i) 3V (2 marks)

      (ii) 4V (2 marks)

The 10k resistor is to be replaced by a variable resistor (potentiometer).

(g) Underline the correct circuit symbol from those shown below. (2 marks)

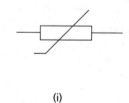 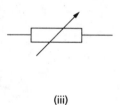

    (i)   (ii)   (iii)

(h) Explain the effect that including this component will have upon the operation of the circuit. (2 marks)

2 (F/H) Part of a circuit which uses a thermistor to control a refrigerator alarm is shown below.

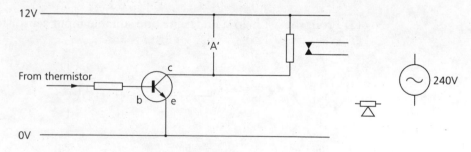

(a) Explain why a refrigerator alarm may be a popular product. (2 marks)

(b) Name the component that needs to be placed at 'A'. (2 marks)

(c) Explain why it is needed. (2 marks)

(d) Complete the connections for the buzzer shown. (2 marks)

Trials have shown that the circuit needs to have a greater amplification. The following modification has been made:

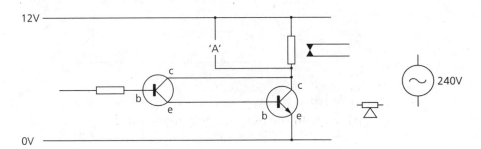

(e) What is the new transistor arrangement called? (2 marks)

The total gain of this circuit is 10,000. The base current I_b for this circuit is 0.000025A.

(f) Calculate the collector current for this circuit. (2 marks)

(g) Calculate the current flowing through the relay if the coil resistance is 600 R. (2 marks)

(h) **Three** different types of relay contacts are shown below. (3 × 2 marks) Name each type.

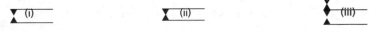

3. (F/H) An NE 555 IC timer is shown below :

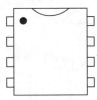

(a) Insert the pin numbers on the diagram above. (2 marks)

The 555 is a CMOS 8 PIN DIL INTEGRATED CIRCUIT.

(b) Explain what the following stand for :

        (i) CMOS (2 marks)
        (ii) DIL (2 marks)

Shown below is a 555 IC astable tone generator circuit :

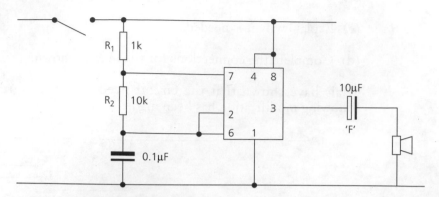

(c) What is the function of the capacitor 'F' in the circuit? (2 marks)

(d) List **four** specification points for the design of a lorry reversing alarm.

(4 marks)

The frequency of the tone generator circuit above is 1 Hertz.

(e) Explain what is meant by the term '*frequency of 1 Hertz*'. (2 marks)

(f) Make **two** changes to the circuit that will result in an increased frequency, giving an explanation of your answers. (6 marks)

4. (H) The circuit symbol for a 741 operational amplifier is given below:

(a) Label all the connections. (4 marks)

(b) Part of a 741 thermostatically controlled comparator circuit is given below:

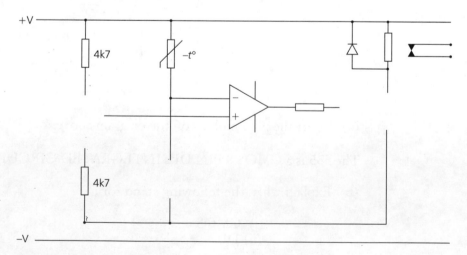

(c) Complete the circuit. (6 marks)

(d) Explain how this circuit works. (4 marks)

An alternative thermostatically controlled circuit uses a 741 operational amplifier in inverting mode.

(e) Complete the connections for this circuit shown below.   (4 marks)

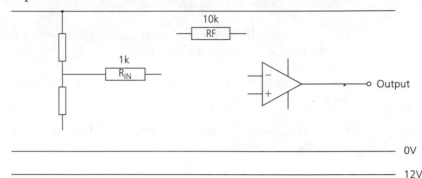

(f) Calculate the Gain of this circuit.   (2 marks)

Food technology

1. (F) Food provides the body with nutrients it needs to sustain it in a healthy condition.

(a) Name **two** nutrients that provide energy.   (2 marks)

(b) Giving examples, explain the purpose of vitamins.   (3 marks)

(c) Dietary fibre is not absorbed by the body. Explain why it is important for a healthy diet to contain dietary fibre.   (3 marks)

(d) Granary bread is higher in fibre than white bread. Give **two** further reasons for using granary bread when making a sandwich.   (2 marks)

2. (F/H) The picture below shows the basic layout for a food label.

(a) What information should be given in the two blank spaces (i) and (ii)   (2 marks)

(b) Describe how the 'list of ingredients' should be arranged.   (3 marks)

(c) Explain the difference between 'Use by' and 'Best before' on shelf life date codes.   (3 marks)

(d) Draw the symbol used on packaging to indicate that the product is 'Suitable for freezing' (2 marks)

3. (F/H) A food company wants to develop a range of pre-prepared packed lunches in boxes for schoolchildren.

(a) You have been asked to prepare a questionnaire to find out what school-children require from such a product.

Give **four** questions you would include in the questionnaire **and** the reason for each. (8 marks)

(b) Give **two** extra questions you would include to be answered by parents **and** the reason for each. (4 marks)

The company uses the results of the questionnaires to make up small batches of sample lunch boxes for testing by schoolchildren.

(c) Describe the difference between 'ranking tests' and 'rating tests'. (3 marks)

(d) A 'star profile' is used to present the result of a rating test.

Draw an example of a star profile **and** explain how it is used to develop the product. (5 marks)

4. (F/H) 'Cook-chill' products have become increasingly popular in our supermarkets.

(a) Describe the 'cook-chill' process. (4 marks)

(b) Explain why food is chilled (2 marks)

(c) If the product is bought on a very hot day, list **four** ways of ensuring that it is safe to eat the next day. (4 marks)

(d) List **four** instructions that you would expect to appear on the packaging of a cook-chill prodcuct. (4 marks)

(e) Discuss the requirements of the packaging for a cook-chill product.

(6 marks)

5. (H) A food production company uses a food safety system called Hazard Analysis and Critical Control Point (HACCP).

(a) Explain what is meant by HACPP. (2 marks)

(b) Explain the difference between quality assurance and quality control. (2 marks)

(c) Explain what is involved in the following methods of production, giving examples of the products most likely to be produced by each method :

(i) One-off (job production) (4 marks)

(ii) Batch (4 marks)

(iii) Repetitive flow (4 marks)

(iv) Continuous flow (4 marks)

Graphic products

1. (F) The diagram below shows a pictorial view of three blocks from a young child's play set.

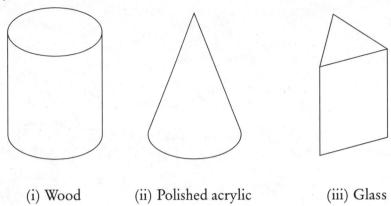

(i) Wood   (ii) Polished acrylic   (iii) Glass

(a) Give the correct geometrical name for each labelled block.   (3 marks)

(b) Taking into account the light source, add colour and shading to make the blocks appear to be made from the specified material.   (7 marks)

2. (F) The use of symbols is very common in everyday life. They are used as warnings, directions and instructions in place of the written word.

(a) Draw **two** ideas – using **black and white** only – for the symbol for a tuck-shop in a school.   (8 marks)

(b) Give two reasons why symbols are used.   (2 marks)

3. (F/H) The table below records the daily sales for an average week of compact discs, computer games and teenage magazines in a High Street store.

	Monday	Tuesday	Wednesday	Thursday	Friday	Saturday
CDs	145	160	155	145	270	420
Computer games	60	60	45	35	105	180
Magazines	305	240	230	205	340	520

You have been asked to prepare a presentation in graph form of these sales figures for the managing director.

(a) Design a **coloured** symbol to represent each of the **three** items, for use on this graph.   (6 marks)

(b) Using the symbols designed in part (a), produce a graph which shows the sales of the three items for the complete week.   (12 marks)

(c) State **two** advantages of using a computer to do this task compared with doing it by hand.   (2 marks)

4. (F/H) The drawing below shows the basic design for the card packet and part of the display rack for a new brand of wild bird seed to be sold in pet shops and supermarkets.

(a) Suggest **four** items that would have been in the specification for the packet.

(4 marks)

(b) Using instruments draw, full size, a development (net) of the final design for the packet. Clearly indicate all glue tabs, fold lines and flaps.   (10 marks)

(c) Give two reasons for selling the product in a packet rather than loose.

(2 marks)

(d) Describe **two** methods of applying the product information to the packet.

(4 marks)

5. (H) The drawing below shows pictorial details of the base pieces for a trophy onto which engraved medallions are later added. The basic outline dimensions only are given.

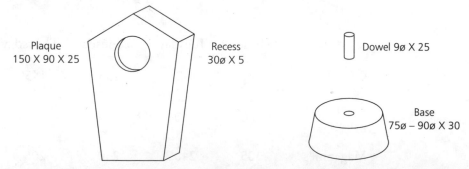

Plaque
150 X 90 X 25

Recess
30ø X 5

Dowel 9ø X 25

Base
75ø – 90ø X 30

(a) Using instruments draw, to a scale of 1 : 2, **three** orthographic views of the **assembled** trophy base in third-angle projection; section **one** of the views.

Hidden detail and dimensions to suit should be included.   (18 marks)

(b) Draw the symbol for third-angle projection.   (2 marks)

Resistant materials technology

1. (F) The picture below shows a hardwood coffee table.

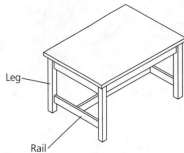

(a) List **three** important pieces of information that would be contained in the specification. (3 marks)

(b) Select **one** of the points listed in part (a) and explain why it is important. (3 marks)

(c) Name **one** suitable hardwood for the table. (2 marks)

(d) Describe **two** properties of this hardwood which make it suitable for use as a coffee table. (4 marks)

The table uses traditional frame joints in its construction.

(e) (i) Name a suitable joint for joining the rail to the leg. (2 marks)

 (ii) Draw and label the joint (6 marks)

2. (F/H) The picture below shows an audio cassette case.

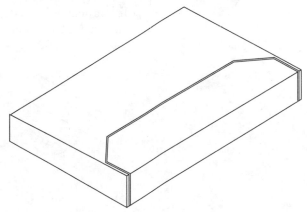

(a) List **four** points that would need to be contained in a detailed specification for this product. (4 marks)

The cases are mass produced using a rigid thermoplastic.

(b) (i) Name **one** suitable thermoplastic that could be used. (2 marks)

 (ii) List **three** properties that make it suitable for such use. (3 marks)

(c) Identify a suitable industrial manufacturing process for the mass production of this product. (2 marks)

(d) Explain why this is a suitable process. (4 marks)

(e) Using labelled sketches, describe the process that would be used. (5 marks)

3. (F/H) The picture shows a young child's toy with moving features that are activated by the pull string.

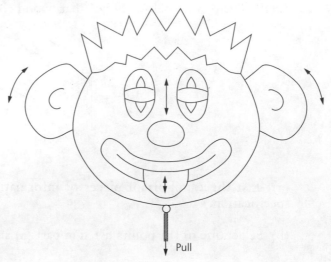

Pull

(a) Explain **two** factors that would be taken into account to ensure the health and safety of a child when using this toy. (4 marks)

(b) Using annotated sketches, design a linkage system that will achieve the movements indicated. (10 marks)

(c) Identify **two** possible weaknesses in this design and suggest ways of overcoming them. (6 marks)

4. (H) The component shown below is to be batch produced, to the following specification :

Tolerance: +/− 0.1 mm
Material: Mild steel
Quantity: 1000

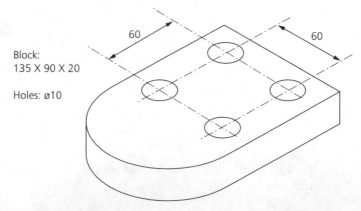

Block:
135 X 90 X 20

Holes: ø10

(a) Explain what is meant by the term 'tolerance : +/− 0.1mm.' (3 marks)

The holes in the component are produced using a jig.

(b) Explain **two** benefits of using a jig for the manufacture of this component. (4 marks)

(c) Using annotated sketches, design a suitable jig for drilling the holes. (10 marks)

(d) Describe **one** quality control technique that would be used in the manufacture of this component. (3 marks)

Textiles technology

1. (F) Large bags, designed to carry items to and from the beach, are popular items sold in seaside souvenir shops. A prototype for such a bag is shown below:

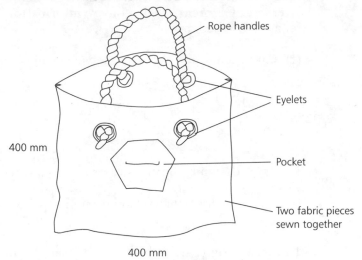

Rope handles

Eyelets

Pocket

Two fabric pieces sewn together

400 mm

400 mm

(a) List **four** points the specification could have included for the bag.   (4 marks)

(b) Suggest **three** features, other than the handle fixing, which could be changed to improve the design of this bag.

Give **one** reason for each change suggested.   (6 marks)

(c) Because of its relative low cost, transparent PVC had been considered as the main material for the bag.

Give **two** disadvantages of using this material.   (2 marks)

(d) The prototype beach bag attaches the handle using eyelets and knots on the rope ends.

Produce labelled sketches of **three** other methods of attaching the handle.   (6 marks)

(e) Give **two** reasons why the two pieces of fabric would be sewn together using double stitched seams.   (2 marks)

2. (F/H) One aspect of textile design is to improve the properties of a fabric to achieve certain working characteristics.

Quilting is a technique for improving the warmth of a garment.

(a) Name **two** textile products that use quilting to improve thermal efficiency.   (2 marks)

(b) Describe quilting and explain how it helps keep things warm.   (4 marks)

(c) Describe **two** problems associated with the process of quilting and how they can be avoided.   (4 marks)

Another important property of a fabric in many situations is its ability to resist catching fire.

(d) Describe a simple experiment to aid the selection of the fabrics to be used in a cot quilt.   (3 marks)

(e) Explain how the flammability of a product can be reduced by chemical treatment.   (3 marks)

Many applied fabric finishes and treatments are affected by the standard of aftercare. Garment labels convey information concerning the correct aftercare required by the fabric.

(f) Give the meaning of the following symbols found on garment labels :

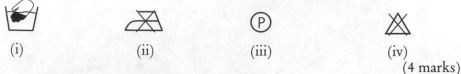

(i)   (ii)   (iii)   (iv)
                                                                              (4 marks)

3. (H) A design company is to produce a sweatshirt for a new leisure centre.

(a) Explain why fashion is important in sportswear, especially to young people.
                                                                              (4 marks)

Two trial designs are to be evaluated using a questionnaire answered by a group of centre members who have been given both of the sweatshirts.

(b) Write **one** question for each of the following criteria :

(i) style   (ii) colour   (iii) comfort   (iv) aftercare   (v) cost   (5 marks)

The results are to be presented to the centre's management committee.

(c) Discuss how the results of the questionnaire can be presented so that they can readily be understood.   (4 marks)

A logo for the leisure centre will also be used on the sweatshirt.

(d) List **four** ways in which computers can assist the designing and manufacturing processes of applying the logo.   (4 marks)

(e) Explain why batch production is the most suitable method for manufacturing the sweatshirt.   (3 marks)

8.6 Specimen answers

Electronic products

1(a) Underline symbol (i)

(b) (i) Light dependent resistor (ii) Thermistor (iii) Microphone (sound sensor)

(iv) Single pole, single throw switch

(c) Transistor

(d) To amplify the current.

(e) A circuit which divides up the voltage according to the ratio of the resistors.

(f) (i) 10k   (ii) 20k

(g) Underline symbol (iii)

(h) Allows the circuit to be adjustable.

2 (a) Reasons could include:

  • saves electricity if the door is left open
  • prevents rotting food if thermostat has failed

(b) Diode

(c) To prevent back EMF which would damage the transistor.

(d)

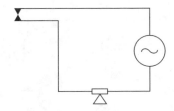

(e) Darlington pair.

(f) $I_c = I_b \times$ Gain (hFE)

  $= 10,000 \times 0.000025$

  $= 0.25\text{A}$

(g) $I = \dfrac{V}{R} = \dfrac{12}{600} = 0.02\text{A} = 20\text{mA}$

(h) (i) Normally open (ii) Normally closed (iii) Changeover

3 (a)

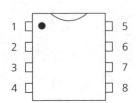

(b) (i) Complementary metal oxide semiconductor   (ii) Dual in line

(c) To store electrical charge – set the time constant.

(d) List could include :

  • operated by microswitch when reverse selected
  • flashing, pulsing circuit
  • audible output
  • control voltage (+12V)
  • small and compact
  • inexpensive

One mark for each of four correct points.

(e) The output will go through one complete cycle (of off and on) once every second.

(f) The only alternatives are to change the resistor values or the capacitor values, making them smaller. Using the Time constant formula $T = C \times R$, any reduction in either C or R will reduce the timing cycle and hence increase the frequency.

Two marks for each change and two marks for a correct explanation.

4 (a)

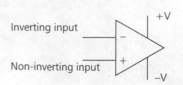

(b)

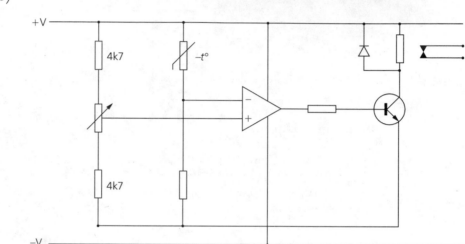

(c) As the temperature rises, the voltage at the thermistor falls. Therefore the voltage on the non-inverting input rises above that on the inverting input. The output switches to +V and the amplifier amplifies the difference between the two inputs.

(d)

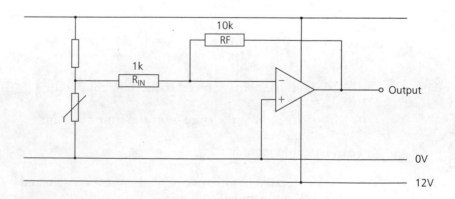

$$\text{(e)} \quad \text{Gain} \; = \; \frac{RF}{R \, \text{in}} = \frac{10}{1} = 10$$

Food technology

1 (a) Carbohydrates, fats, proteins.

One mark for each of two.

(b) Vitamins maintain body tissue and processes, e.g. Vitamin A promotes healthy skin and Vitamin C aids the absorption of iron.

One mark for the explanation and one mark for each of two correct examples.

(c) Dietary fibre absorbs water, adds bulk and thus helps avoid constipation.

One to three marks for a clear explanation.

(d) Adds texture, flavour and colour contrast.

One mark for each of two reasons.

2 (a) (i) Nutrition information
(ii) Weight or volume of product

One mark for each correct answer.

(b) Should be arranged:

- in descending order of weight
- with additives having their correct name or E number
- with type of additive indicated

One to three marks for a description depending on clarity and completeness.

(c) 'Use before' is for highly perishable goods that are usually only chilled and are likely to deteriorate rapidly after the date shown. 'Best before' is used for longer-lasting items – up to eighteen months.

One to three marks for an explanation depending on the clarity of the distinction between the two.

(d)

One or two marks.

3 (a) Questions / reasons could include:

Where do you eat your lunch?– to find out if eating implements need to be included
How long do you take to eat your lunch? – possible digestion problems
Is this your main meal of the day? – possible range of sizes to be provided
Have you any special dietary needs? – should these be catered for?
Can you get a drink at lunchtime? – to see if a drink should be included
What type of bread do you prefer? – health considerations
What type of fillings do you dislike? – to avoid waste and lack of success for the product

One mark for each of four appropriate questions and associated reasons.

(b) Question/reasons could include:

How much would you be prepared to pay? – to evaluate the costing implications for the product
How often would you buy the product? – to evaluate potential sales
What would you want included? – to ascertain differences between parent and child's wishes

One mark for each of two appropriate questions and associated reasons.

(c) 'Ranking tests' ask the testers to simply put the samples in rank order of preference, often based on only one criterion. 'Rating tests' ask the testers to put a numerical score on a number of criteria for each of the samples, e.g. sweetness, salt content, texture. etc.

One to three marks for a description of each test which clearly distinguishes between them.

(d)

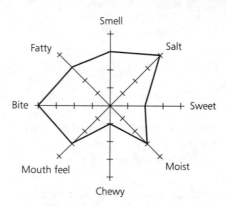

The profile gives clear information about the characteristics of a product which can then be adjusted accordingly in specific areas.

One to three marks for the drawing showing:

- labelled arms
- numbered graduations
- joined to form a 'star'

One or two marks for the explanation.

4 (a) The product is prepared and cooked in the normal way but is then rapidly chilled to just above freezing point and maintained below 5 °C. It must be thoroughly reheated immediately it is removed from refrigeration and before eating.

One to four marks depending on completeness of description.

(b) It halts growth of bacteria and thus prolongs storage life. The method produces the best quality convenience food as it is prepared in the normal way.

One or two marks.

(c) The list could include
- transport in a cool bag
- keep in a refrigerator below 5 °C
- follow cooking instructions, especially heating temperature
- reheat only once

One mark for each of four correct points.

(d) The list could include:

- use by date
- keep refrigerated below 5 °C
- if to be stored in a freezer, freeze immediately
- thaw before cooking
- consume within 24 hrs after defrosting

One mark for each of four correct points.

(e) Discussion points could include :

- main container suitable for oven and/or microwave
- main container suitable for vacuum packing
- outer wrapping must protect product
- suitable for freezing
- outer package must be printed
- must not increase weight unduly
- easy to handle and store

One to six marks based on quality of discussion and points included.

5 (a) HACCP is a system of control used to make sure that a product is safe, legal and consistent, involving identifying potential hazards and implementing controls which eliminate or reduce the risks.

One or two marks.

(b) Quality control means checking for accuracy – e.g. weight of ingredients, cooking temperatures, whilst quality assurance means building in procedures which ensure quality is achieved.

One or two marks.

(c) (i) Used when one or very few, often hand-crafted, items are required – e.g. special-occasion cakes.

(ii) A low-level production method where some time-saving devices can be used, often by a small team with individual responsibilities for different parts – e.g. family baker.

(iii) Where large numbers are required in repeat batches. Often more automation employed on a production line basis. Requires greater organisation due to scale, e.g. packet foods.

(iv) Used for extremely large output, usually continuous and highly automated and expensive if stopped for any reason. High initial cost to set up, but cost effective to run – e.g. soft drinks.

One to three marks for each depending on understanding and depth of answer – plus one mark for each depending on the examples given.

Graphics products

1 (a) (i) Cylinder (ii) Cone   (iii) Prism (triangular).

One mark for each correct answer.

(b) One or two marks for the rendering to achieve each of the material effects, plus one mark for shading.

2 (a) One or two marks for the quality of the two drawings, plus one or two marks for the effectiveness of each of the two symbols.

(b) Reasons could include :

- overcomes language problems
- suitable for those who cannot read
- quicker to understand than the written word
- more readily understood from a distance
- often saves space

One mark for each of two correct reasons.

3 (a) One or two marks for a suitable symbol for each of the three items.

(b) One or two marks for the accuracy of each of the three 'sales lines'.
One, two or three marks for the clarity with which the graph can be read.
One, two or three marks for the effectiveness of the presentation.

(c) Advantages could include :

- data errors can be easily changed
- speed of production once data has been put in
- more accurate if data is correct
- wide variety of presentation methods available in spreadsheet programmes
- once set up, it can be used for the data from other weeks' sales

One mark for each of two reasons.

4 (a) The items for the specification could include :

- will be made from one piece of card
- will contain 500g
- will show the contents when on display
- will tessellate to save space when transported
- will hang from a hook or rod type stand

One mark for each of four correct items.

(b)

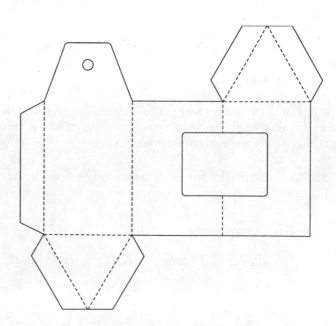

One to four marks for the basic development – including the hanger.
One or two marks for the window.
One or two marks for the fold lines.
One or two marks for the glue tabs/flaps.

(c) Reasons could include :

- easier to store, with less health risk from vermin
- easier to handle and sell
- more convenient and attractive to the customer
- more profit made

One mark for each of two correct reasons.

(d) Print directly onto the card before assembly
    Print onto a label and attach

One mark for each reason.

5 (a)

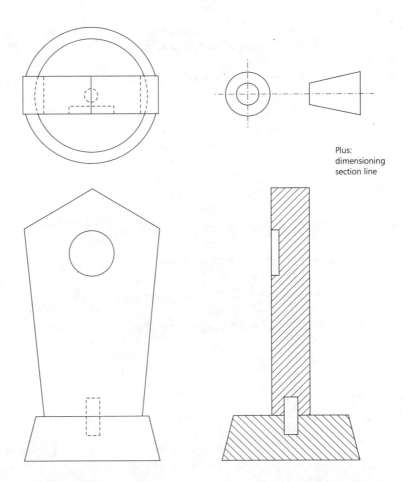

Plus:
dimensioning
section line

One to three marks for the construction of each of the three views (9 marks in total)
One or two marks for the correct arrangement of the views.
One to three marks for the sectioning.
One mark for hidden detail.
One to three marks for the dimensioning.

(b) Two marks for the correct symbol.

Resistant materials technology

1 (a) Information for the specification could include :

- height
- length
- width
- material
- finish
- cost

One mark for each of three points listed.

(b) One mark for selecting the point and two marks for a correct explanation.

(c) Suitable hardwoods could include :

- oak
- ash
- teak
- mahogany
- beech

Two marks for a correctly named hardwood.

(d) Properties, depending on hardwood named, could include :

- grain gives good appearance and colour
- strength, in terms of stability if seasoned well
- close grained, does not split easily
- good working characteristics

One mark for each correct property.

(e) (i) Named joints could include :

- mortise and tenon
- dowelled
- tee halving

Two marks for a correctly named joint.

(ii)

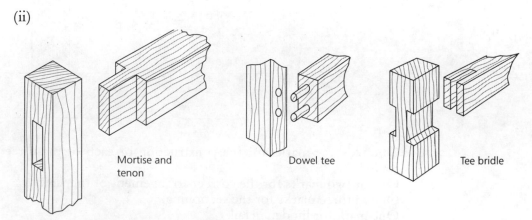

Mortise and tenon   Dowel tee   Tee bridle

Six marks for a clear drawing of the joint named, correctly labelled.

2 (a) Specification points could include :

- material and properties
- sizes
- must accommodate visible insert
- stackable
- able to be numbered
- cheap to produce in large quantities

One mark for each of four points.

(b) Rigid thermoplastic, e.g. PVC, acrylic

(c) Injection moulding.

(d) An explanation which includes two of the following:

- economically more viable the larger the number
- good dimensional accuracy and consistency
- good finish
- speed of manufacture

Two marks for each of two points explained.

(e) Granules of thermoplastic are heated until molten and injected under extremely high pressure into a split mould. The pressure is maintained whilst the mould is rapidly cooled. When the plastic has solidified, the mould is opened and the moulding ejected. See Chapter 3 for drawing.

Two marks for a correct sketch with three marks for labels and description.

3 (a) Safety features to include :

- no pieces with sharp edges which could cause cuts
- no toxic finishes to be applied that could poison if swallowed
- no pieces included capable of being swallowed
- avoid finger traps
- avoid brittle materials capable of being bitten off and swallowed

Two marks for each of two points explained.

(b) In order to obtain the full ten marks, the following will need to be evident:

- a range of sketches
- clearly and correctly annotated
- a system that works

It should be noted that part marks will always be awarded for partially correct or even incomplete answers.

(c) Weaknesses could include :

- snagging
- non-return
- no stops
- rubbing points

One mark for each of two weaknesses and one mark for each modification.

4 (a) The allowed deviation above or below a stated size or dimension.

One to three marks depending on the completeness of the definition.

(b) Benefits could include :

- accuracy as it avoids marking out
- consistent duplication due to pre-setting of jig
- speed or production increased due to no marking out
- reduced operator skill level

One or two marks for each of two points explained.

(c) In order to obtain the full ten marks, the following will need to be evident:

- a range of sketches
- clearly and correctly annotated
- a system that works in that it locates and clamps the work given rounded shape
- hardened steel inserts to avoid wear at drilling points

It should be noted that part marks will always be awarded for partially correct or even incomplete answers.

(d) Quality control techniques could include :

- hole gauge for checking hole diameters
- shape template for checking radius
- alignment gauge for checking hole positions
- micrometer and vernier gauges for material dimensions

One mark for the process and two marks for the description.

Textiles technology

1 (a) Points could have included :

- size
- material
- number required
- target cost
- manufacturing method
- added features, e.g. pocket

One mark for each valid point.

(b) Suggestions could include :

- more comfortable handle for easier carrying
- fastener to close top
- add zip to make pocket more secure
- add gusset to increase capacity
- add other decorations to improve appeal

One mark for each of three improvements and one for appropriate reason.

(c) Disadvantages could include :

- tears easily if punctured
- degrades in heat and sunlight
- machines poorly
- contents of bag visible

One mark for each of two reasons.

(d) Other methods could include :

- rivets, box stitched with a cross inside
- D-rings and fabric tabs
- buckles
- drawstring

One mark for each of three appropriate sketches plus one mark for labelling.

(e) Reasons could include :

- added strength
- harder wearing
- cut edges are enclosed to stop fraying
- can be done in one operation

One mark for each of two reasons.

2 (a) Products could include :

- oven gloves
- tea cosies
- duvets
- muffs
- ski jackets

One mark for each of two correct items.

(b) Layers of fabric are built up with a central wadding layer between the main fabrics. Lines of stitching are applied in the form of checks, stripes, lozenges or motifs. Air is then trapped in the 'bulging' layers which improves insulation.

Three marks for the description and one for the explanation.

(c) Problems and their solutions could include :

- puckering of main fabric during stitching – correct foot pressure, adequate pinning
- slippage of fabric against wadding – adequate pinning, allowance of extra which can be removed
- inaccurate pattern of stitching – careful marking out

One mark for each of two problems and one for their solutions.

(d) Cut strips of fabric and hang securely. Hold a lighted taper to the fabric for a few seconds and remove. Record speed of burning, colour of flame, amount and colour of smoke and residue. The results for the different fabrics are compared with special regard to speed of burning and toxicity of fumes. Decisions can then be made on selection and finish treatment.

Two marks for a clear description of the experiment and one mark for reference to how this aids selection of fabric and surface treatment.

(e) Application of flame-retardant chemicals, e.g. Proban, with the addition of fire warning labels and detailed washing instructions.

One mark for the explanation, plus one mark for naming a detergent and one mark for other relevant information.

(f) (i) Hand wash only   (ii) Do not iron   (iii) Dry clean   (iv) Do not bleach

One mark for each correct meaning.

3 (a) Heavily influenced by advertising, peer group pressure, image and identity and the link with professional stars. Sportswear is also regularly used as everyday wear.

One to four marks depending on the number of relevant points made in the explanation – a minimum of three points required for full marks.

(b) One mark for a question suitable for each criterion that generates a comparison between the two sweatshirts.

(c) The discussion should include the following points:

  • the results need to be recorded
  • visual methods of presentation discussed, e.g. bar charts, graphs, etc.
  • use of computers to assist this
  • conclusion arrived at

One to four marks depending on the number of relevant points made in the discussion – a minimum of three points required for full marks.

(d) List could include :

  • ease of changing design features for evaluation - colours, size, shape
  • ease of producing drafts
  • analysis of manufacturing requirements
  • ease of machine embroidery
  • accuracy of repetition
  • less skilled production labour required

One mark for each of four relevant ways

(e) The numbers required will not be suitable for larger scale production, but the features make it suitable to take advantage of some aspects of automation, e.g. machine embroidery. It also allows for repeat batches to be easily produced, should the sweatshirt prove popular.

One to three marks depending on the quality of explanation and examples used – a minimum of two examples required for full marks.

Glossary

A

Absorbency The ability to absorb liquid.

Acrylic A plastic, referred to as PMMA, but commonly known as Perspex.

Additives Synthetic or natural chemicals used in food production to colour, preserve and enhance flavour. Additives approved by the EU have an E number.

Adhesive A bonding agent used to join materials.

Advertising A means of promoting a product.

Aeration Lightening by incorporating air.

Aesthetics How various features combine to make something 'beautiful' or 'attractive' (see also **Formal elements**).

Alloy A combination of two or more pure metals, or one or more pure metals mixed with other elements, to produce a metal with different properties.

Amino-acids Chains of protein molecules essential for life and obtained from food.

Ampere (Amp) Unit of electrical current.

Analyse To reduce to basic elements – a term often used in the early stages of the design process.

Annealing A softening process using heat to allow easier working – especially of metals.

Anthropometrics The study of the measurements of human beings and their movements.

Anti-static Treatment to prevent the accumulation of electric charge.

Artefact A product designed and made.

Astable (pulse generator) A system whose output continually switches from high to low.

B

Bacteria Micro-organisms present all around us, capable of multiplying and causing disease.

Batch production The limited production of a number of identical artefacts.

BDMS Bright drawn mild steel.

Bearing A device which reduces friction in moving parts.

Bias An oblique line across the grain of textiles – 45° to the selvedge.

Biotechnology Biological processes used industrially.

Bistable (flip flop) A device which will 'latch on' until reset – used for counting or storing a signal (see also **Latch**)

Blanch To immerse briefly in boiling water to stop enzyme spoiling of fresh food such as vegetables.

Bleaching To improve the whiteness of a textile.

Blend To mix different constituents into an homogeneous whole.

Blow moulding A common industrial plastic moulding process used for products such as bottles and barrels.

Brainstorming A rapid collection of initial thoughts regarding a problem.

Brief A clear statement of the problem area.

Brushed fabric To raise the pile by brushing to increase thermal properties.

BSI British Standards Institution – the organisation responsible for preparing codes of practice.

Bulked fabric Fabric treated to add volume without adding weight.

C

CAD Computer-aided design.

CAD/CAM An integrated system of design and manufacture using computers.

Calendering Passing between heavy rollers to flatten or give lustre.

Calorie A unit used to measure the energy values of foods.

CAM Computer-aided manufacture.

Carbohydrate Source of energy found mainly in sugars and starch.

Carding Straightening of fibres prior to further processing.

Ceramic A kiln-fired clay product.

Cholesterol A fatty substance, part of every living cell.

CNC Computer-numerical control.

Closed loop A control system where feedback constantly alters the process to maintain the specification and quality.

Colour fast A dye that does not fade when washed.

Compression moulding A volume production process used with thermosetting plastics.

Conductor A device that conducts electricity.

Conservation The protection of the natural environment and its resources, involving the reduction in the use of raw materials, recycling of materials and concern about the methods of production used.

Constraints Limits placed on the design process.

Consumer A person who purchases or uses a product or service.

Cook chill Food preparation involving rapid cooling after cooking and keeping for short periods in chilled storage before reheating.

Corporate identity The 'whole' graphic image of a business or organisation – the logo type, uniform, colour, product image(s).

Corrosion Gradual deterioration of metals.

Criteria Working characteristics that a product or process must achieve.

Critical control points Stages in a production process that are regularly checked to ensure errors and risks are reduced to an acceptable level.

Cross-contamination Transfer of microbes from one substance to another.

D

Danger zone The temperature range in which bacteria multiply 5–63 °C.

Darlington pair A two-transistor system used to produce a high gain, high power circuit.

Data Relevant facts and figures collected by research or experimentation and testing.

Database A collection of information, now commonly stored on computer.

Demand The quantity of a product required by the consumer.

Denier The weight in grammes of 9000m of yarn or filament.

Design The process of solving problems through the development of ideas to produce a solution within set constraints.

Development (1) The refinement of ideas to produce a solution. (2) The flat form of the surface area of a container (sometimes known as a net).

Dietary fibre The indigestible carbohydrates found in plant food. Also referred to as non-starch polysaccharide (NSP).

Disaccharides Sugars such as maltose and sucrose.

Draft A feature of a pattern for sand casting or vacuum forming ensuring easy removal – also known as the draw angle.

Ductility The ability of a material to be drawn out without breaking.

Dye A colouring agent.

E

Economies of scale The cost of a single unit will reduce as more are produced.

Efficiency The reduction of wasted resources – time, energy, material, etc.

Emulsion A mixture of fats and liquid which does not separate.

Environment The surroundings in which we live and work.

Enzyme A protein that controls the rate of chemical reactions in the metabolism of living organisms.

Ergonomics The study of human interaction with the environment.

Evaluation Judgements made throughout the design process which test the outcome against the specification.

Exploded view A three-dimensional drawing with the individual components drawn in their relative positions but not fully assembled.

Extrusion A moulding process commonly used with aluminium and thermoplastics.

F

Fabric A woven or knitted material.

Farad The unit of capacitance.

Fat A source of energy made up of fatty acids.

Feedback Information, gained by monitoring systems, that is used to regulate the production process.

Fibre Thread-like material used for spinning yarns. Short fibres, natural or synthetic filaments cut up, are known as *staple fibres*.

Fibreglass Commonly known as GRP (glass reinforced polyester).

Filament A fibre of indefinite length.

Finish The surface treatment of a material to improve the appearance and durability.

Fixed costs The costs that a company has to expend regardless of output.

Flow chart A diagrammatic representation of a process which includes decision making and feedback.

Food poisoning Illness caused by bacteria and other poisons in food.

Formal elements The part of aesthetics that relates to the common elements of visual appeal – colour, shape, form, balance, symmetry, composition, line, rhythm, proportion.

Former A predetermined shape around which a material such as acrylic is shaped.

Formulation The ratio, type and mix of ingredients.

Function What an artefact or process is expected to do.

G

Garnish An edible decoration giving colour to food.

Generic Of the same group or family.

Gluten The substance giving flour mixtures elasticity.

Glucose A simple sugar.

Grain The arrangement and size of constituent particles in wood, metal and fabric.

Gross The total without deductions.

H

Hardening Cast steel is heated and cooled quickly in tepid water or oil.

HACCP Hazard analysis and critical control points –a system for monitoring food safety.

HBV High biological value proteins that contain enough of all the essential amino-acids.

Hertz The unit of frequency.

Hydration Adding liquid.

Hygiene A regime of cleanliness to reduce the risk of food poisoning.

I

Impedance The internal resistance of a device.

Injection moulding The injection of a molten material into a mould under pressure.

Insulator A device that has a very high electrical resistance.

Intrinsic sugars Natural sugars contained in milk, fruit and vegetables.

Isometric A method of drawing objects in three dimensions using vertical and 30° axes.

J

Joining The fastening together of constituent parts.

K

Kilo Used in conjunction with other units to signify 1000.

L

Laminate Build up by layering.

Latch A device or circuit which when triggered will hold itself in the condition until externally reset (see **Bistable**).

Logo Symbol associated with the identity of a company or organisation.

M

Malleable Easily worked without breaking – often with the application of heat.

MAFF Ministry of Agriculture, Fisheries and Food.

MAP Modified atmosphere packaging, which seals food in an atmosphere other than air to stop bacterial multiplication.

Marketing The selling of a product or service to the consumer.

Mass production The production in large numbers of an artefact.

Minerals Elements and chemicals naturally present in small quantities in food, necessary for a healthy life.

Mock up A model – often full size – of a design to allow evaluation.

Monostable A circuit which when triggered will switch to output high for a predetermined time – then reset itself.

Multimeter Device for measuring voltage current and resistance.

N

Nap   Raised pile on a fabric.
Needs   The essential requirements of life.
Net   The total after deductions.
Nutrients   Food components that provide energy and aid growth.

O

Oblique   A form of three-dimensional drawing.
Ohm   The unit of resistance.
Operational amplifier   A differential voltage amplifier – the most common being the 741 type.
Organoleptic   Affecting the senses.
Orthographic   A form of technical drawing usually consisting of three views drawn to scale, projected at 90° to each other.
Overheads   Costs not directly related to the manufacture of a product.
Oxidation   The reaction of the surface of some materials with oxygen in the atmosphere.

P

PAR   Planed all round – with reference to prepared timber.
Perspective   The appearance objects give of being smaller, the further away from the viewer they are.
Plastic memory   The ability of some materials to return to the shape they were before moulding, once they have been reheated.
Polymer   Long chain molecules that form the main structure of plastics.
Potential difference   Often referred to as voltage.
Potentiometer   Another name for a variable resistor.
Preservatives   Chemicals that prevent other materials from deteriorating in the atmosphere.
Primary processing   Conversion of raw materials into food stuffs.
Primary research   Research done personally by you from original sources.
Profit   The difference between the cost of production, including overheads, and the selling price.
Properties   Physical and working characteristics.
Proportion   The due relation of one thing to another.

Prototype   The initial version of a product used for testing, development and evaluation.

Q

Quality control   Operational techniques that ensure the process performs to specification.
Questionnaire   A survey made up of a number of related questions given to people in order that their views may be analysed.

R

RDA   Recommended daily amount of energy and nutrients required from a healthy diet.
Recipe   Otherwise known as formulation.
Research   The gathering of information.
Resources   Equipment, materials, knowledge and skills you have to draw on.
Retail   The merchandising of products.
Risk   The likelihood of a hazard occurring.

S

Sample   A group selected to represent the majority.
Scale   Representing dimensions on a drawing in proportion – greater or smaller – to the actual ones
Scaling up   Increasing quantities in the prototype for mass production.
Seasoning   (1) Controlled drying of green timber to render it suitable for use in manufacture. (2) The adding of salt, pepper, herbs and spices to food.
Secondary processing   The conversion of the products of primary processing.
Secondary Research   drawn from existing sources, e.g. books and magazines.
Selvedge   The longitudinal edges of woven fabrics which give strength to facilitate further processing.
Semiconductor   A device that conducts electricity (usually) in one direction only, dependent on its internal construction.
Sensory analysis   A method for scientifically evaluating reactions to food characteristics.
Shelf life   The period that a food product can safely be stored under the correct conditions.

Silver solder An alloy of silver, zinc, copper and cadmium which melts at a higher temperature than tin/lead solder.

Solution The means by which the need is satisfied.

Specification The criteria that the solution must achieve.

Spider diagram A means of presenting the results of brainstorming.

Supply The amount of a product available at one time.

Survey Research carried out by questioning.

Starch A carbohydrate which forms the basis of many diets.

Structure An arrangement of members designed to resist a load.

Synthetic Not occurring naturally (man-made).

System A group of processes organised to perform a task.

T

Testing Checking the outcome in relation to the specification.

Time constant The time taken for a capacitor to charge to 0.7% of the supply voltage.

Toggle mechanism A device which allows the quick locking and release of a clamp.

Transducer A device that converts one form of energy into a different form.

TVP Textured vegetable protein, manufactured from soya beans as an alternative to meat.

U

Unit cost The cost of producing a single item, found by dividing the total costs by the number of units produced.

V

Vacuum forming The process of shaping thermoplastics onto a former by the application of heat and a vacuum.

Vitamins Compounds, obtained from food, necessary for normal growth and health.

Volt The unit of electrical pressure.

W

Warp The longitudinal threads in a woven fabric.

Watt The unit of power (amps × volts).

Weave A method of fabric construction using two threads.

Weft Threads going across a woven fabric.

Weld Joining similar materials by melting them together using heat or chemicals.

Y

Yarn A thread made from spun fibres.

Index